Australia
2000!

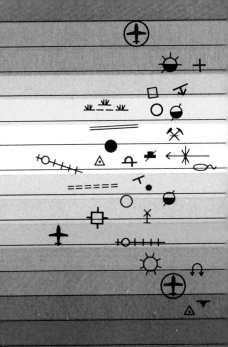

Australia

by DON FABUN

2000!

A LOOK AT ALTERNATIVE FUTURES

Assisted by Kathy Mackay
Raynette Page and Dorene Errichetti
Design by Fetzer-Conover Graphics
Production by Al Reisser

THE FREE PRESS
A Divison of Macmillan Publishing Co., Inc.
New York

All rights reserved. No part of this book
may be reproduced or transmitted in any
form or by any means, electronic or
mechanical, including photocopying,
recording or by any information storage
and retrieval system, without permission
in writing from the Publisher.

THE FREE PRESS

A Division of Macmillan Publishing Co., Inc.
866 Third Avenue, New York 10022

ISBN 0.02.910190.5
Library of Congress Catalog Card
Number: 74-1482

First published 1974
Cassell Australia Limited

Printed and bound in Hong Kong

Dedication:

To Alex McGoldrick and his family;
Dee and Sally and Richard and
Katie, including a female cat
somehow named "Ned Kelly," who
was dumb enough to lie right
behind the wicket in the backyard when the ball was bowled.
**Most particularly to Katie,
a five-year-old who will shake
the world of AUSTRALIA 2000!**

   **After all, it will
   be her world.**

**And—to my wife,
Gladys, who shared
the whole, magnificent,
five year adventure.**

Acknowledgements:

Where does one start and where does one end?
There were so many kind and friendly people, so many places, so many times, over a span of nearly four years, that it is impossible to include them all here. Australia may be a strange land, but with the help of these people, one was never a stranger there.

Whatever follows may seem completely incoherent and in no particular order of importance; they were *all* important:

They range from such friendly people as a constable in Belmont, whose office was a little table in his backyard where he sat sipping beer in the sun and waiting for the phone to ring. . . .

To a station owner in Moola Boola who spent the fire-rimmed night, his whisky in front of him, recalling more than half a century of life by a lonely man on a cattle station spread over a million and a half acres. . . .

To a bush pilot flying from Cairns to Weipa who allowed a bloody Yank to "help fly" a tiny little plane loaded with an oil drill pipe that took up all the aisle space between the seats. . . .

To an innkeeper in Perth who took the money for a set of cafe table lights, but never did get around to delivering them. . . .

To a young and pretty stewardess who pointed out where the "facilities" were on Barrow Island—two empty oil drums. She was going to show off the three little trees the island supports—but time ran out. All the rest was bare and burning rock.

To a lonely Irishman, John Morris, on holiday from the mines at Mt. Isa, who wanted to know if by any chance one had ever heard of a couple of countrymen of his, named George Bernard Shaw and Oscar Wilde. We had, we had. . . .

To a very harried man on Green Island, Al Miller, who ran a giant aquarium almost single-handedly, picked up deadly stone fish in his bare hands, and taught one more about the Great Barrier Reef in a few weeks than most people would learn in a lifetime. He could have worn a crown of thorns starfish on his head. . . .

To a cab driver in Brisbane who knew all of the koala at Lone Pine Sanctuary, fondled them softly, and even let a stranger pet them. . . .

To a young man, David Frost, who drove one endlessly through the vast Snowy Mountains, pointing out the little wild things no casual tourist would ever see. . . .

To so many—cab drivers, train conductors, bush pilots, stewardesses, hotel maids, groundskeepers, bar maids, ranch hands and miners, wool gatherers, construction workers, bowlers and cricketers, students and professors, artists and actors and musicians, business executives and newspapers editors—to so many. One owes them all a profound gratitude and certainly this very unsubstantial acknowledgment. This book grew out of their hopes and aspirations, out of their fears and their doubts, out of their isolation and loneliness, and out of their willingness to share their enormous room with a stranger from outerspace.

Equally important, of course, are the professionals. Without exception one found them warm and friendly and totally immersed in the great adventure that is Australia. To mention a few:

Prof. Adrien Albert, Australian National University, John Curtin School of Medical Research, Canberra; a world authority in his field in chemistry and in sterile laboratory research.

Mr. A. W. Charles, assistant secretary, Agricultural and Biological Sciences Branch, and **Dr. J. Barry Allen,** assistant secretary, Industrial and Physical Science Branch, Commonwealth Scientific and Industrial Research Organization, both at Campbell, A.C.T., who opened up the whole vast labyrinth of the CSIRO for interviews and material.

Mr. Harry P. Black, head press officer, CSIRO, Campbell, A.C.T., and his assistant **Miss Wendy Parsons,** who set up interviews with CSIRO experts throughout Australia and furnished reams of technical and scientific information in dozens of research fields. . . .

Prof. Stephen Boyden, biologist and environmentalist, Australian National University, Canberra, an expert on the interaction between the life forms and the land in Australia. . . .

Mr. Joe Colgan, director of public information, Department of Minerals and Energy, who furnished many maps and pertinent background about nearly every phase of Australia's people, its resources and its economy. His headquarters are in Canberra.

Dr. Alec Costin, plant ecologist, Division of Plant Industry, CSIRO and co-editor of a highly regarded book, *Conservation,* which served as a catalyst for many of the ideas in this book and who offered many personal observations on the Australian view of ecology and its probable consequences for the future. He's at Black Mountain, A.C.T.

Sir George Currie, Kt., now retired in Deakin, Canberra; historian, philosopher, scientist, academician and a leading authority on Papua/New Guinea. He is an authority on science and the Commonwealth government.

Mr. Peter Dawe, chief librarian, CSIRO, Melbourne, opened the doors to the vast library of CSIRO pamphlets and publications covering virtually every aspect of Australian scientific research and technological application.

Mr. John Gilmour, former financial editor of *The Financial Review,* for days, while driving on winding, sleet-slick roads in New Zealand, gave one deep insight into the Australian financial system and its probable futures.

Dr. Ivan Newnham, M.B.E., director, Mineral Research Laboratories, CSIRO, Melbourne, gave much valuable information on the Australian development of the beach and sand minerals, rutile zirconium and titanium.

Dr. Phillip G. Law, C.B.E., Melbourne, ex-director of the Antarctica Division, Department of External Affairs, world expert on Antarctica, and author of *ANTARCTICA — 1984* gave much valuable first hand information on that continent and its future possibilities.

Mr. Alex McGoldrick, assistant secretary, commodity policy division, Department of Overseas

Trade, Canberra, virtually converted the American author into an Australian by making him a member of his family and by opening his mind and heart to the complex questions considered in this book. He also made many high level contacts possible that otherwise would not have been.

Dr. Ray Perry, chief, Rangelands Research Unit, Division of Land Research, CSIRO, Black Mountain, A.C.T., gave much valuable insight into rangeland and grazeland research and development and its probable future.

Sir Clarence Byrne, Kt., O.B.E., D.S.C., now retired in Caloundra on the Queensland coast, is knowledgeable in the mining and metals industry and is a philosopher as well. He kindly reviewed the outline for this book (sitting on the grounds of his estate with the great

Australian surf pounding in) and made many excellent suggestions.

Sir Henry Beaufort Somerset, Kt., C.B.E., in Melbourne, a conservationist, former chairman or director of major cement, pulp and paper mills and president of the Australasian Institute of Mining and Metallurgy, who gave valuable insights into the future of these industries.

Sir Frederick White, K.B.E., C.B.E., F.R.S., chairman of the Commonwealth Scientific and Industrial Research Organization for many years and a world authority on radar physics and electromagnetic wave phenomena. He lives in Red Hill, A.C.T.

Dr. Paul Wild, chief, Division of Radiophysics, CSIRO, Sydney; world authority on organic particles in space and galactic chemistry. He is a living demonstration of the brilliant quality of Australian research in far-out fields.

Mr. Bob Winkworth, scientist, Rangelands Research Unit, Division of Land Research, CSIRO, at Black Mountain. He knows the soils of agricultural Australia like the back of his hand. And is willing to share his knowledge.

Mssrs. **Dean Bunney, David Rowntree, Paul Clarkson, Ian Head** and **Peter Allen,** worked wonders to furnish transportation and accommodation facilities for trips that covered tens of thousands of miles and lasted for months at a time. They handled mail and packages, and secured the legal clearances for the artwork and quotations used in this book. Without their help, the whole mission would have been impossible.

Real "mateship!" ■

Contents:

You are about to embark upon a voyage aboard a very strange craft engaged in a multidimensional exploration in space and time.

You might consider it as a sort of floating laboratory that forms the superstructure for a great stone raft called Australia.

Entries in the log go something like this:

They are the descendents of the turbulent world of the European 18th Century. Today, some of them are the malcontents from 20th Century Europe. Now what will they do, this motley crew?

The immigrants — the number of them — "populate or perish" vs. "zero population" — the urban concentration along the southeast coastline — who is to be allowed in — the coloured and the bearded — and what about the original all-black crew? What will happen to it?

Some sort of collective consciousness, it seems. It may not know where it is going, but it knows where it has been. Standing at the wheel, the daydreams are of home in England and Ireland and Scotland. The nightdreams are haunted by a black presence; a ghost that walks the quarterdeck. What's the course, mate? Forward! Aye, aye, sir.

Stranger in a strange land — Hedonism — "Shall we have fun?" vs. "Shall we dress for dinner?" — Nationalism — the flag says "Australia Fair" — Gambling — "Give 'er a go" — Strains from the "Third World Theme" — The Multi-Faceted Man — seadog, bushman, digger, mateship and the classless society. And loneliness seeping in from the north, like a chill wind.

It bores steadily northward, this child of the ancient continents of Pangaea and Gondwanaland. Its sister ship, India, left home long ago, and behind there is only the cold and icy image of grandfather, Antarctica. The stone raft dips in the seas of time, scooping up an extraordinary array of mineral and metal riches. Enough to fill a global pirate's chest. Yo-Ho! Now who's to share and how much for each?

Some billion-year-old accounts of Pangaea and Gondwanaland — the anchored iceberg — energy sources, atomic, solar, wind tides, petroleum and coal — water resources — fossilized aquifers, sub-surface, surface, water rainfall — reducing salinity — soil management — grazelands — dominant land use — mineral extraction: iron ore, bauxite, copper, lead, zinc, gold, silver, zirconium, titanium, opals, uranium.

No vessel is safe without a dog. Henry Lawson provides one. Look out! It's "The Loaded Dog." Run for your lives, mates!

A flashing glimpse into the Australian mind: its Devil-May-Care attitude, its constant feeling of impending calamity, and its rollicking sense of humor. Written about 1885, and as pertinent today as it was then.

Some puckish crewman scribbled the name "Antarctica" over the door. Inside, encased in ice was the history of the most probable future. No crewman knew the combination to the door yet, but someone was sure to find it. Once inside, what would one do?

A sterile laboratory for the study of viruses — genetic engineering — sperm banks to preserve endangered species — cryobanks for human organs and bodies — icy caverns for burial of nuclear wastes — testing labs for space and electronic equipment — a listening spot for the solar winds — an exciting tourist attraction.

There in the back of the Captain's cabin was a veritable treasure chest. Open the lid and

find ransom for a king. Iron—
bauxite—copper—manganese—
nickel—lead—zinc—gold—
silver—zirconium—titanium—
uranium—coal—oil and gas.
The chest seemed bottomless.
Only the years would tell.

6. THE ENGINE ROOM: *page 101*

It was hot down there; the
continent roasted like a lamb on
a spit. The rocks for ballast
grew hot as coals. The sands
for the fire dampening glowed.
The only rain was the perspira-
tion of the engine room crew.
"If anything can help him now—
the kind old sun will know."
Locked in a solar cell—the
corrugated manses—empty can
technology—a sun space-mirror
—space enough and time.

THE RADIO SHACK: *page 108*

It is required by international
maritime law that all ocean-
going vessels have a way to
communicate with the shore and
with other ships. The Stone
Raft built its "radio shack" in
the form of a "Singing String"
all the way from Sydney to
Java, a distance of 4,500 miles.

7 IN THE STORE ROOM: *page 113*

Such a profusion of sheep,
lambs, cattle, goats, kangaroos
and wallabies, swinging from
their ecologic hooks, one could
hardly believe. In the corners
were wines and fruits, and
vegetables, wheat and rice in
overflowing bins. No crew
member would go hungry;
not on a thirty-year voyage,
anyway.

8 THE WHEELHOUSE: *page 131*

Steady as she goes! Chart a
course for the world. Be
another Captain Cook. Try the
winds of fortune and the reefs of
time. Try new passages in the
future dark, and show other
ships the way. Let other peoples
and nations take a turn at the
wheel. Give them the use of all
those empty rooms to do all
those economic, political and
social experiments for which
they have no room to try at
home.

**The laboratory of the world—vast
inland areas—off-shore islands—a
climatic range from the tropics to
the arctic—monitoring and guidance
from highly proficient scientists and
technicians—space and resources
for "model cities"—places to experiment with population densities—
environmental control—ecological
studies—interconnected transportation systems—self-reinforcing
communication systems—government by direct participation through
satellites and electronics—an array
of different lifestyles—so many
things that could be worked out
over the decades for all the people
on the globe.**

9. FUTURE PORTS OF CALL: *page 169*

Two great organisms roamed the
vast decks of Australasia, playing
a future game in the enormous
room. In the taxonomy of the
day they had been labeled
CSIRO and NAT/DEV:
creatures of enormous potential.
As they danced their *pas de
deux* to the music of a changing
world their eyes were focussed
a thousand years from now,
and their hands were busy with
the present. On things like: cattle
bloat and plastic capsules—a
bird too frequent—radiating
pine trees—seeds that needed
an overcoat—how to hang a
carcass in a chill room—making
friends with white ants—and a
sort of transcendental goal:
"to do things men have never
done before."

And that, sir, is quite a course
to follow. ■

Introduction:

Like a painting or a sculpture or a piece of music, if a book needs an introduction, it probably should not have been written in the first place.

However, a blank page is irresistible to an author; nature and writers abhor a vacuum. It is as compulsive to fill the empty pages as it is, for some, to write graffiti on the walls of time.

So, by way of introduction, here are some graffiti:

FIRE IN THE NIGHT

MOOLA BOOLA: You don't know where Moola Boola is? Why, it's only 17 miles by Land Rover from Hall's Creek.

From Hall's Creek? That's only 135 miles from Christmas Creek. By air, of course. Both are on the northern edge of the Great Sandy desert, south of the Kimberley Range. The closest town is Darwin, 685 miles to the north. The closest city is Perth, 1800 miles away. Moola Boola can be a kind of lonesome place.

Moola Boola means "much beef," and indeed, the 45,000 head roaming the 1,600,000 acres of the station are much beef, particularly since there has been no rain for 14 months, and the cattle are gathered around the water holes, not much bigger than a bath tub. They mill and shoulder each other in the dust.

This particular time was midnight and temperature about 90 degrees. You can hear the cattle lowing, crying out to great storm clouds boiling up over the Kimberleys.

There is a fire out there—it has been burning. now for five days on a 20-mile front, giving a crimson rim to the northern sky. There is no way to stop it; there aren't half a dozen people in the whole area. The fire will burn itself out, someday.

Sitting there at a table outside the veranda of the station, in the heat of the night, sipping warm Australian beer, there is suddenly a drop of rain landing splat! And that was all the sky-water one was going to see for many more weeks.

The early morning sky as clear as crystal. Covered with flies and dust, one bounced along in the Land Rover; priming the pumps with kerosene, using the 30.06 to shoot the cattle too weak to make it to the water holes. The crows and the parrots waiting expectantly.

Back in the Land Rover, spewing clouds of dust behind. The sun is molten iron flowing in the sky. It is only 7 a.m From now on, nothing but the sun and flies and heat and dust until the clouds boil up again over the Kimberleys. Perhaps, there will be a drop of rain tonight, and the cattle will cry again. The fire will still be burning the bush in the north.

And the men will sit and wait for better times.

A NIGHT TO REMEMBER

DARWIN: It is possible to go further north on the continent, but it is not advisable. For a hot, miserable and utterly lovely place, Darwin can hold its own. Port Moresby in New Guinea comes thundering down the stretch as a close second.

Anyway, the plane from Darwin to Adelaide leaves at the convenient time of 2:30 a.m. At least it's cool then, only about 100°. One makes arrangements with one of the two taxi companies for a ride to the airport at 1 a.m. But it fails to show. Time running out and the next plane doesn't leave until next Thursday. One finally gets another cab and races to the airport. Plane already on the runway, loading ramp being removed.

A shout in the darkness. Now running pell-mell with bags in hand. Ramp shoved back in place. Breathless in the hot and humid air, bags trundled up the boarding ramp and tossed into the vestibule. Ramp backed away, engines revving up. We're off!

But one had made it. Thanks to a cab driver who risked his life to make a 35 minute trip to the airport in 20 minutes. To airline attendants who waved one through to the runway. To runway attendants who pushed the loading ramp back in the darkness. To a pilot who waited for the crazy American to scramble aboard.

And that was Australia— always a helping hand. And a voice calling from a darkened seat saying, "She'll be right, Mate!"

And so it was.

TARANTULAS FOR BREAKFAST

GREEN ISLAND: Not a very big island (38 acres overall) basking on the back of the Great Barrier Reef, about 17 miles offshore from Cairns in North Queensland. It is ringed by coral sand beaches as white as snow, encircled by jade-green waters shading off to indigo. The waters dance with shimmering schools of silver fish. The island itself is covered with tropical rain-forest, the trees adorned by flocks of white cockatoos like Christmas tree ornaments. It looks (and is) like something a Hollywood producer might have dreamed up. Many Australians

take holiday there, sharing the dream.

But this little adventure was something else. In the house one was staying in, there were other, more permanent residents. Tarantulas big around as a saucer. (Actually, they were Huntsman Spiders, who can, and do, kill and eat full grown birds.) Humans owned the place by day, but the tarantulas ruled it by night.

In the early morning hours, one could shine a flashlight around the room and there would be a sudden scurrying of furry somethings; Exodus revisited.

There was one, though, that did not run away. He preferred living in one's slipper under the bed at night. His name (though he didn't know it) was George. One quickly learned to shake one's slippers out before putting them on in the blackness of a tropical morning. George, being evicted, always scuttled into the closet. One also learned to shake out one's clothes before putting them on.

There also was a more academic type that seemed addicted to reading and usually could be found by flashlight, crouching on a book next to the typewriter on the kitchen table. He'd scurry to sulk under the refrigerator.

The tarantulas never came into the bathroom; that was reserved for giant (three inch) cock-roaches. An early morning exercise was to throw wadded up toilet tissue at them. They were not as fast as the tarantulas, and so made a nice, fat, slow-moving target for the early morning sportsman. They rowed their many-legged way, antennae waving, under the kitchen sink,

waiting for breakfast.

Tell you, never a dull day on Green Island.

GREAT DAY IN THE MORNING

CAIRNS: The day starts early. By noon one could fry an egg on one's bald head. If one had an egg and a head.

This was a special occasion: "Rats of Tobruk Day." One walked out of The Great Northern Hotel in the early light and heard bagpipes and drums approaching. Having nothing better to do at that time in the morning in Cairns, one investigated, and there, coming down the one and only main street, was a straggly group of beerpot-bellied middle-aged gents, driven like a flock of sheep down the sidewalk by a brilliantly-garbed—kilts and all— Scottish pipe and drum band. Followed by dogs nipping at their heels. Followed by a lonesome stranger who got up too early.

This unlikely parade staggered its way down a main street to the square, a journey of just a few minutes, and gathered in front of a statue of a World War I Anzac soldier.

A vast throng of perhaps two dozen people had gathered there, most of them waiting for the pub to open. The mayor arrived and made a rather long speech concerning the patriotic reasons for re-electing him and mentioned Tobruk reverently. The crowd, leaning against the front of the pub, shifted its feet with shattering ennui. A couple of the dogs got into a fight, enlivening the ceremony some.

When the mayor finally finished, a very young and

embarrassed soldier stepped forward, looking for all the world the living image of the Anzac statue he had been guarding, then lunged forward and fired a single round into the air from his World War I Enfield rifle.

The uniformed color guard marched smartly forward, and to the strains of what could have been "God Save the Queen" (one can never know with bagpipes) the Flag was ceremoniously raised high on the flag pole, rippling grandly in the morning trade wind.

It was upside down!

Never mind, most of the vast crowd had already disappeared into the pub. To be quickly followed by the remnants of Tobruk, and strange looking people in kilts carrying bagpipes and drums, and an American observer who thought it had been the grandest parade he'd ever seen.

Now the sun was over the yard arm, and The Day was over. The dogs snuffled at the pub door, not being licensed to enter licensed premises.

A VOYAGE TO THE CENTER OF THE EARTH

BROKEN HILL: It was rather early in the morning and one was whisked away to one of the mines, which, legend has it, were started by a burro a century or so ago. (He was kicking up his heels and dislodged a rock that turned out to be nearly pure silver.)

Anyway, once there, one was led to a locker room; stripped, and put on a heavy canvas suit of overalls, safety glasses, a hard

hat with a miner's lamp on it, knee-high boots and a pair of gloves whose gauntlets reached to the elbow.

Looking and feeling like a man from Mars, one entered a great iron cage of an elevator. It dropped like a rock down a shaft where water spurted from crevices through the steel mesh of the cage. The lift stopped at a tunnel 2400 feet beneath the surface; a flight that took one-and-a-half minutes.

Now a long walk along a railroad track in a dimly-lit tunnel that dripped, and then a climb up flimsy wooden ladders in total darkness. The miner's lamp was a feeble glow, and one's booted feet fumbled at the slippery rungs and one's heavily-gloved hands hung on for dear life.

Finally there. It was a working stop on the seventh level. Now on hands and knees crawling up a jet black tunnel, and across a narrow plank bridge, with a thousand-foot drop below. Now some light. Here was a large chamber where two young Australians—nearly naked— crouched and directed a bangity-bang sort of scoop shovel that clawed at the walls, knocked down ore, scooped the broken pieces up, dragged them back and dumped them down the "glory hole," (the one the narrow plank crossed) to land in an ore car ten stories below.

The young men shouted curses at each other, with the steel wires singing softly of death, and the rumble of the shining silver ore tumbling like a thunderous cataract down the shaft.

For twelve hours, these two descendants of the heroes of

Tobruk sweated in the semi-darkness. They would get eleven cents a ton for all the ore they knocked down, raked out, and dropped down the shaft. Not bad, really; they could make as much as $32 a day, if they lasted that long, plus·their room and board. They were proud because they were Australians, and brave because they were young.

Feeling one's age, one gingerly felt one's way down the slippery ladders in the dark, and headed for the iron cage, which voyaged upward through the impromptu showers bursting from the rock, as quickly as it had come down.

Dress and walk outside to the brilliant greens and sunshine of the other world. . . .

The whole voyage had taken less than an hour.

Now, all of this was long away and far ago.

What does any of it have to do with the theme of a book about the future of Australia? Goodness only knows. Except that if one does not personally know the land, nor its people, nor whence they came, it is a little presumptuous to come up with the graffito:

"AUSTRALIA—2000!"

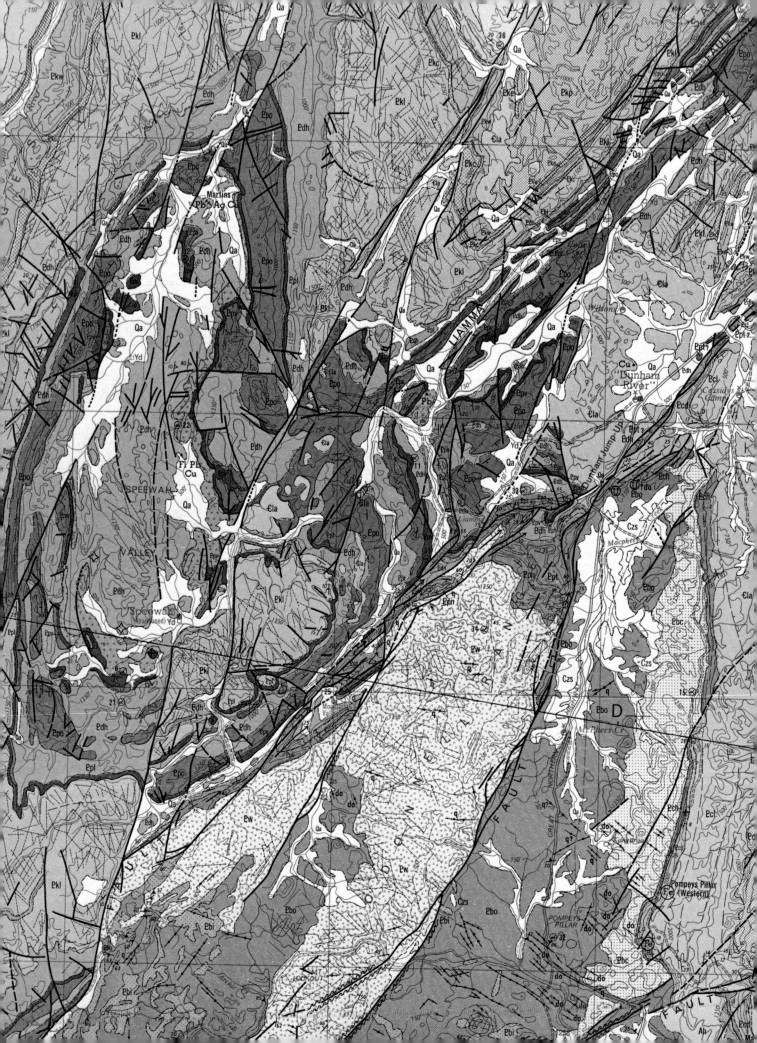

The man walked a little slowly through the floating laboratory, because he had been skipper for about 150 years and things had not always been easy for him. He had ridden out the storms of time, but they had taken their toll.

This stone raft, with its laboratory super-structure, was also kind of old; it had been plowing northward for some three billion years or so.

He brushed the cobwebs from his mind and began his morning inspection. He checked the chill box, labeled Antarctica. Seemed cold enough, all right. He examined the engine room temperatures on gauges labeled Northern Territory, Queensland and New Guinea. Seemed hot enough, all right.

Back on the main deck, he stopped to wash his hands in the water flowing down the sink, labeled the Murray River; he rinsed them off at a tap called The Ross and dried them over the radiator warmed by The Centre.

And then he mounted the bridge.

One of the first things he did in the morning was to count heads, because the basic decision for Australia is—how many? For quite a long time he had lived with a general policy of "Populate or Perish!" It made sense for a time, in a harsh and hostile country. But perhaps no longer. Do more people really increase the quality of life? Or, by dividing up the natural resources, so that more have less, decrease it? Or does anyone know? The nearly empty corridors echo no answer.

Anyway, there seemed to be 12,800,000 people on deck this morning.

Not very many for an area equal to one-fourth of the globe. He overlooked Antarctica. There were 23 Australians there, but most were going to come back shortly.

He shook his head, and, thinking about the year 2000, which was a convenient benchmark in his scheme of things, he tried to figure out, in a sort of computer-wise fashion, what might happen to the population there in the laboratory by that time. What alternatives were open?

Well, of course, one could just go muddling along in the same old way. The formula was a pretty simple one. Almost 2% growth per year. That would yield a population of some 22 to 25 million by 2000 A.D. There was a controllable variable there—immigration. Say about a quarter of the overall growth. One could just open and close the valves and so come out at either the 22 or 25 million level. Without doing very much at all. That would be the easiest way.

If long-term movements are examined, natural increase has contributed far more to growth in the last hundred years than has immigration.
—*Population Increase and Decrease* 1947-1954; Atlas of Australian Resources; Department of National Development, Canberra, 1958

But there were other alternatives, and these deserved attention, too.

For instance, one could implement a "zero population growth" policy. In which case, by the year 2000, the population would be about the same as it was at the moment.

It may be true that Australia can carry a population much larger than the present one because of unexploited resources and the potential for "an expanding international trading system based largely on Asia." It may also be a good idea to utilize more of this capacity.
On the other hand, there are strong arguments for pressing for the greatest possible reduction in growth rates everywhere, including Australia.
—DR. K. A. W. CROOK, President Society for Social Responsibility in Science, Australian National University; *Canberra Times*, Nov. 17, 1971

With a large (33%) Catholic population and one out of every six in the population immigrants from Europe—both groups believing in large families—it was difficult to see how this could be done. Even if it could be, would it be desirable? And desirable for whom? People take deep pleasure in their children. How is the quality of life improved by denying this pleasure? A question, but no answer.

A study of world population statistics shows that the three areas which have experienced massive population increases since the 1930's are Africa, India and China . . . Now we are hearing the argument that because of overpopulation in Asian and African areas, and the demands of American affluence and military expenditure, it is incumbent on us to reduce our own population growth to zero, frowning on motherhood and ceasing immigration . . .
The incidental fact that the increase in the Chinese population in one year is considerably more than the total Australian population does not apparently cut much ice, as far as the relative curbing of the two populations is concerned.
—*THE NATIONAL TIMES*, Monday, December 13, 1971

Australia most urban of nations —survey

From PETER SMARK: LONDON, MONDAY

AUSTRALIA is the most urban society in the world with 88.5 per cent of its population living in cities, according to a survey by the Organisation for Economic Co-operation and Development.

Although Japan is catching up fast, Australia is likely to remain the country with the highest per-

12,728,461 of us

AUSTRALIA'S population increased by almost 10 per cent during the past five years, and in June this year stood at 12,728,461.

This is shown in the preliminary figures from the 1971 census of population and housing released in Canberra yesterday by the acting Commonwealth Statistician, Mr J. P. O'Neill.

They show the Northern Territory, the A.C.T. and Western Australia have the fastest-growing populations in the country.

Need for doubling population seen

Well, suppose instead you decided greatly to increase the immigration. This might be made necessary anyway as the result of world trade pressures and global politics. For instance, the exportation of primary industry products—such as wool, meat, grains and minerals—might have to be based on a much less rigid immigration policy than now exists, particularly as regards non-whites and non-Europeans. Australia has no monopoly on these basic agricultural items, and it is at least possible that the buying nations might ask, as part of the contract, relaxed immigration policies before they order. Assuming this might be true, the result would not only be quantitative, but qualitative. Many new customs, mores, types of dress, kinds of foods, language accents, etc., would be introduced. This might enrich the complexity of life-styles, but also might destroy a homogeneous culture that takes pride in its homogeneity.

From July 1, 1947, to June 30, 1969, there was a total net immigration to Australia of 2,080,000 persons . . . In terms of ethnic origin, 38 percent were from the British Isles and 52 percent were from continental Europe. Just under a quarter of the Continental Europeans were from northern Europe (Germany, the Netherlands, Scandinavia, Austria, Switzerland, etc.), over a quarter were from eastern Europe (Poland, Yugoslavia, the Baltic States, Hungary, the U.S.S.R., etc.) and almost half came from southern Europe (Greece, Italy, Malta, etc.).
—*Immigration: Atlas of Australian Resources*, Second Series, Department of National Development, Canberra, 1970.

A record baby boom
But families are not getting bigger

AUSTRALIA is experiencing an unprecedented baby boom.

The Royal Women's Hospital Melbourne, in the year until June 30, yesterday reported the biggest increase — 964 — with the Crown Street Women's Hospital Sydney, the runner-up.

The births at Crown Street, totalled 7113, 710 more than for the previous record year 1961-62.

The story is much the same at major women's hospitals in all capital cities, and according to Professor W. D. Borrie, head of the research school of social sciences at the Australian National University, Canberra, is likely to continue for some years.

Professor Borrie says the present increase in births is the direct result of the baby boom which followed the end of World War II: the children born in those immediate postwar years are now having children of their own.

There were 257,000 births in Austra-

lia last year, and Professor Borrie calculates that if present immigration and fertility levels remain about the same, 331,000 babies will be born in 1980, and 361,000 in 1985.

But, says Professor Borrie, although there are more women of childbearing age in the population than

ever before, there is no evidence that the size of families is increasing.

The head of the department of obstetrics and gynaecology at Sydney University Professor Rodney Shearman, said the birth rate remained about 20 or 21 per thousand population. It had hovered between 17 and 21 per thousand since before

Perhaps immigration could be tailored so that it satisfied market demands and provided some bright threads of color in the fabric of Australian life, but would leave the existing society mostly intact. Ah, but who would determine how many and what?

> What is needed, and what is now happening, is for us to learn also from them. Our own sometimes harsh outlines can be softened and refined by sympathetic absorption of other multicoloured and memorable pasts. Memory is the vital agent which helps us explore and define new worlds —their memories as well as ours.
> —ROBERT R. GOODMAN/GEORGE JOHNSTON: *The Australians*, Rigby, Ltd., James Place, Adelaide, 1966

All of these assumptions were obviously based on another assumption—yet to be proven—that somehow or other the Australians could determine their own population density and mix within the next thirty years. There is nothing in Australia's past or present that indicates that it can control this aspect of its future.

> More striking than any common characteristics of the colonists, however, were the distinctive peculiarities of the different national groups: English, Irish, Scottish and non-British. Of these, the various foreign migrants exerted minor influences as individuals, not as a group. Each of the three British elements of the people, on the other hand, including a minor Welsh group, brought its own national character, religion, politics, outlook and habits, whilst each displayed special traits as the country itself brought its pressure to bear on them.
> —T. INGLIS MOORE: *Social Patterns in Australian Literature*, Angus and Robertson, Pty., Ltd., Sydney, 1971

Among the less happy prospects was that the continent might be infiltrated by Asiatics pushed down from the North by population pressures there. This could be done in a most informal manner, small boats in the night, landing people at random so they could take up residence at obscure points along the coast. They could slip along New Guinea, island-hopping, and make it ashore almost anywhere along the beaches of the Gulf of Carpentaria and Darwin, or land on the seaward coast of North Queensland, then push slowly south over several decades.

The impact of one more baby

SIR, — Your editorial, "Dr Ehrlich's Itinerary" ("The National Times," December 13-18), provides a most valuable service in drawing again to the community's attention the problems of over-population.

While it is correct in pointing out that migration is of relatively small significance as a factor of population growth, it avoids the basic problem — "natural" growth, ie. growth within the indigenous population — and plays down the significance developed countries, which should set proper examples, including that of stable population.

PAUL SINCLAIR,
Turramurra, NSW.

Keep Australia's population small

SIR. — I was disappointed to read your editorial ("The National Times," December 13-18) on Dr Ehrlich's recent visit. You talk as if our raison d'etre in this country is to fully populate it as quickly

It seemed an unlikely probability, because, except for the giant prawns in Carpentaria, and a few wallaby on the land, there would be little to live on. The country there is hot, barren and hostile. It is subject to very violent storms, torrential rains that turn dry courses into rivers miles wide and 50 feet deep. Or no rains at all for months on end. Beyond the coast, hundreds of miles of sand and sun-baked rock, where it takes 40 acres to support one kangaroo.

No, it did not seem that peaceful infiltration from the North would pose much of a problem. Except for some people.

The fear of Chinese immigration which the Australian democracy cherishes, and which Englishmen at home find it hard to understand, is, in fact, the instinct of self-preservation, quickened by experience. We know that coloured and white labour cannot exist side by side; we are well aware that China can swamp us with a single year's surplus of population; and we know that if national existence is sacrificed to the working of a few mines and sugar plantations, it is not the Englishman in Australia alone, but the whole, civilized world, that will be the losers.
— *The Boomerang,* Nov. 19, 1887

What did seem more likely though, was the possible takeover of the continent by some major world power. (One remembers the peaceful, but disruptive, "invasion" of the Yanks in World War II.) Valiant as they may be, there would be just too few Australians to defend their territory. In an I.C.B.M. and nuclear weapons age (they have neither), the Australians' protection lies solely in the help they can get from allies. The problem, if indeed there was one, lay in political skills rather than military prowess.

The array of political alliances would become increasingly important as Australia became the fulcrum for the Pacific Basin balance of power between Russia, the U. S., Europe and Asia.

The second world war weakened considerably the British element in the already diminished clash of cultures in two ways: it taught Australians a hitherto neglected lesson in geography, making them aware that they lived in the Pacific and Indian oceans close to Asian neighbors and must reckon with Asia; it drove home the harsh fact that their survival as a free people depended upon aid, not from London, but from Washington.
— T. INGLIS MOORE: *Social Patterns in Australian Literature,* Angus and Robertson, Pty., Ltd., Sydney, 1971

In this game of kings and bishops, Australia would be but a pawn, even if it doubled or tripled its population by the year 2000. Its survival as an entity would depend on the skill of its statesmen in negotiating foreign alliances.

There was, of course, still another possibility. As the result of a global nuclear war, which it could not precipitate and in which it could not participate, Australia might well not have any inhabitants at all—a condition it would share with all the other continents except, perhaps, Africa and South America.

Very soon, perhaps in a month's time, there would be no one here, no living creatures but the cats and dogs that had been granted a short reprieve. Soon they, too, would be gone; summers and winters would pass by and these houses and streets would know them. . . The human race was to be wiped out and the world made clean again for wiser occupants. . . Well, probably that made sense.
— NEVIL SHUTE: *On the Beach,* Wm. Heinemann Ltd., London, 1957

Zero population, indeed!

These are not all of the future alternatives. There is always the trickster lurking in the background that no one can foresee until he plays his game.

> It is as if at our backs, masked and demonic, moved the trickster as I have seen his role performed among the remnant of a savage people long ago. It was that of the jokester present at the most devout of ceremonies. This creature never laughed; he never made a sound. Painted in black, he followed silently behind the officiating priest, mimicking, with the added flourish of a little whip, the gestures of the devout one. His timed and stylized posturing conveyed a derision infinitely more formidable than actual laughter.
> —LOREN EISELEY: *The Unexpected Universe*, Harcourt, Brace and World, N. Y., 1964

This concept had been brilliantly portrayed in an Australian stage play—"The Legend of King O'Malley." In this, O'Malley, having failed to convert the members of the Waterlilly Rock-Bound Church, meeting in the Redskin Temple of the Cayuse Nation (somewhere near Waco, Texas) decided to make a run for it, and took off in his thoughtfully-built coffin from California to Australia. His black shaman paddled him all the way. O'Malley arrived on the northern coast of Queensland, and with his black witch doctor jeering and playing tricks behind his back, finally worked his way south and started the trade-union movement in Australia.

Although purely Australian, "The Legend of King O'Malley" encompassed the whole human condition.

However logical or articulate humans may think themselves to be, there seemed to be a dark force behind their backs that would thwart the most valiant efforts of the white man. Someone from Vienna named Freud pointed that out some time ago. (Shaman you!)

But, getting back to the population bit, combining several of the alternatives could result in a different population "mix" by the year 2000. Of course, it would not be a population "mix"; they would all be human beings, regardless of color, sex, or national origin. But it would take some people a little while to accept that.

Or perhaps there might be future alternatives hardly even dreamed of.

There could be an invasion from outer space, which seems rather unlikely, or a plague, or the continent just sinking quietly into the sea on which it floated. Again, not likely within thirty years. Still, this is the "Unpredictable Continent" and, historically at least, it has been shown that anything can happen here.

What did seem to be important was that Australia, alone among the continents (except for Antarctica, which could be considered a part of it), still had the option to determine how many people it wanted, and what kind of people. It might very well decide to stay pretty much the way it was. When it looked around the world, it did not find anything better.

Perhaps this was the world's last hope for mankind; this eerie continent of forgotten animals, lost races of man, and stars like diamonds in the sky. It was almost the last place one could see them any more.

In addition to the quantitative and qualitative problems, there was that of distribution; where to put this little mob of people on this vast station. Most of them had huddled on the southeast coast. There, nearly three quarters of all the white Australians lived.

As in many other parts of the world, this concentration served no discernibly useful purpose—political, communicative or economic. The urban areas had, however, created problems of mental health, automobile traffic, air and water pollution and considerable environmental land damage. This was a curious thing to contemplate, because the Australians already had before them innumerable illustrations—in North and South America, in the U. K., in Europe, Russia, the Middle East and Asia—that the city as an instrument for modern life was a failure. They, the Australians, alone were born in a world that could provide technological ways to avoid the city and to develop a 21st Century society.

In the outback, they did, to the extent that they used radio and aircraft and finally television, to create a social order that was highly communicative, although widely dispersed.

The Anglo-Australian has perished or is absorbed in the Interiors much more rapidly than on the seaslope and in the towns . . .
Where the marine rainfall flags out and is lost, a new climate, and, in a certain sense, a new race begins to unfold itself . . .
The one powerful and unique national type yet produced in Australia is—that of the Bushman.
—FRANCIS ADAMS, *The Australians*, London, 1893

Goodness knows there was plenty of land. But neither the cities nor the government recognized that they had within their grasp the only 20th Century lifestyle in the world that could bypass all the ancient errors.

The growth rate of Perth was 2.9 percent a year and the city conforms to the general pattern of population change observed earlier among the other capital cities, i.e., there was a loss of population in the inner city and gains on the outskirts.
—*Population Distribution and Growth*, Atlas of Australian Resources, Second Series, Department of National Development, Canberra, 1964

Still, it was not too late.

Many alternatives remained for the solution of population distribution problems.

Through the use of atomic power (Australia had the richest uranium deposits so far discovered) it should have been possible to establish model cities anywhere in the continent. Deep bore wells could bring up "fossil water" trapped for eons below the continental mantle. These same atomic plants could furnish electrical power, and their hot water wastes could be used for hydroponic vegetable farms and for high density tropical food fish ponds. That's inland. The technology already existed. The capitalization didn't, but in collaboration with foreign investments, it very well could.

These nuclear plants could furnish the water, power and food supplies for "model cities" of "optimum" size—whatever model and·optimum may mean. "Optimum" had yet to be defined. How many people, in what sized area, at what density, could be governed efficiently with existing or modified institutions? Nobody seemed to know, but there might be foreign countries willing to finance the experiments to find out; using their own people, leasing unoccupied areas, perhaps monitored by Australian technicians, projects covering one or two generations. Why not?

On the coasts, atomic energy plants could desalt sea water, use the by-products (chlorine, sodium, magnesium, etc.) as marketable industrial products; use the power, in part, to pump the fresh water inland a hundred miles or so. This alone, just a few atomic plants, would expand the habitable area of Australia by about 20 percent.

The 1971 census appears to give weight to the estimates made recently by a firm of consultants which suggested that Darwin may have a population of between 192,000 and 214,000 by 1990 and Alice Springs by then may have between 41,000 and 53,000 inhabitants.
(In 1971, Darwin had a population of 35,281 and Alice had a population of 11,118).
—G. J. R. LINGE, Professorial Fellow, Department of Human Geography, Australian National University, *Financial Review*, January 6, 1972

Suppose one put the interior and coastal systems—atomic plants and model cities—into interacting systems? What then?

What might happen was that one could have an electronically dispersed "cottage industry" in which many people now in the urban centers could produce at home; thus avoiding commuting, traffic congestion, highway accidents and smog. An end devoutly to be hoped.

Their products, and in many cases, their services, could be brought to market by smog-free electric vans, or flown to market by smog-free atomic aircraft. The products also might be transmitted through the conversion of energy into matter. The theoretical basis was there, the technology was not, but it might well be by the year 2000.

How would such "cottage industries" work? Nobody knew, but the Australians had the land, the people and the technology to find out. Again, other countries might be willing to pitch in to finance ten to twenty-year programs, to see if "cottage industries" on an electronic grid system, would work.

There were other alternatives. The cities could just decide not to grow anymore, to restrict or forbid private automobiles to central city areas, and to restructure high density centers into medium density centers, and to get rid of the suburban scatter altogether, returning large areas of the land to productive or recreational uses.

9

Flora Eldershaw, discussing the modern landscape writers as part of the continuance and renewal of the folklore element said truly of them: Varied though their approach may be, together they give a romantic vision of a world with which many men secretly or openly want to identify themselves, the unique Australian world that is the possession and kingdom of our imagination. We, a small people, can say: "We have this strange, this antique, still virgin world; it is ours." They are wonder books... They are about *us*, even if we are townsmen.

T. INGLIS MOORE
Social Patterns in Australian Literature
Angus and Robertson, Pty. Ltd., Sydney, 1971

L. Buvelo
Winter Morning Near Heidelberg

These options were open to many countries, but lack of land space, population densities, cultural and ethnic considerations, religious and nationalistic pressures, made it politically and economically impossible for them.

But this was not true of Australia. It had the land, it had the technology, and only a minimum of ethnic, religious and political hangups to restrain it from free experimentation in lifestyles, at many levels, in all sorts of environments. Here, truly, could be the laboratory of the world!

Humans had, traditionally, been preoccupied by production (more people, more artifacts) and seldom with distribution (where to put them, and how to get them there). There remained, for Australia alone perhaps, to find out how these two systems could be made to work easily with each other. Could there be a more important role in a materialistic world than that?

The problem of population "mix" was the most difficult of all. The white Australian was proud of his whiteness. He also was proud that he had been able to keep an essentially white European culture alive and well in a strange, isolated, often hostile country. That this had resulted in a great sameness of culture did not bother him as much as the possibility that it might change through the absorption of significant numbers of people with other ways of thinking and doing things. It was seldom in his scheme to think of Australia as a "melting pot."

Foreigners—particularly those of a different color of skin—tended to form ghettos whose lifestyle was different from, and therefore seemed to threaten, a traditional way of life. Immigration of nonwhites could create the kind of racial problems the United States and the United Kingdom were already facing. Why go through all that again? With the mechanization of construction, mining and agriculture, there was little need for "cheap" labor of the sort the U. S. had needed in a pre-industrial, pre-technological era. True, there was not enough service help—people to make beds in hotels, wash dishes, shine shoes, rake lawns or carry luggage at transportation terminals. But people to do this kind of work could always be recruited from Europe, and still keep the country white.

This is what most Australians probably wanted and would do. And, of course, it was *their* country (or so they felt) and within that context, they had every "right" to choose what sort of neighbors they wanted to live with.

Assisted migration involves freedom of choice in a desire to move by the migrant but, in contrast to unassisted migration, employment obligations for two years after migration were involved until 1952. After that date, no occupational obligations to employers, government or other organizations were enforced. However, assisted migrants are still under an obligation to repay to the Australian Government the amount of passage assistance granted to them if they leave Australia within two years of their arrival . . .
— Immigration: *Atlas of Australian Resources,* Second Series, Department of National Development, Canberra, 1970

One could question such a policy on moral or intellectual grounds, but such questions were likely to be more academic than realistic. The Australians were not English, as they liked to think they were— cold toast, elaborate place settings spread on the table cloth, tea, lawn bowling, cricket and the rest—nor American—which they most desperately did not want to be. They were Australians and would make their own decisions in the way that would best protect their way of life, which was the best in the world for the majority of its people.

Migration from eastern Europe has included a special variant of the assisted form: refugee migration. Refugee migration involves a forced exodus from a person's country of origin to avoid persecution for political or ideological reasons. Thus, refugees often have no capital or possessions on arrival and, if assisted by government or international organizations . . . may have to work for a period in employment specified by the host country's government.
— Immigration: *Atlas of Australian Resources,* Second Series, Department of National Development, Canberra, 1970

Well, what alternatives remained open to them on this highly complex and controversial question?

They could, of course, continue present policies of a rigid determinism, which largely excluded people of nonwhite, non-European descent or restricted entry of "undesirables"—such as those with beards and long hair. The difficulty with this kind

migrants
Poor refugees toil to repay fares and live

THOUSANDS of poverty-stricken migrants who come each year from the Middle East and Asia have to repay fares of up to $1800 while wealthy Europeans can migrate for $20 each.

The poor migrants, including refugees, are sponsored as unassisted migrants by church agencies. Many arrive with no money. The agencies only lend them the fare.

About 800 migrants from India last year could bring only $7 each with them because of India's ban on taking currency out of the country.

The migrants, who earn usually between $40 and $70 a week, pay up to $20 a month off their fares debt, depending on their capacity to pay.

A Burmese family of seven reached Perth with $25.

A refugee family from the Middle East which arrived in Sydney with no money pay $26 a week rent.

The father, in an effort to support his five children, worked a 12-hour day and for a short while earned $90 a week, until he fell ill from overwork.

Tough

Another Middle East family, including four children, pays $30 rent in Sydney, although the father, a laborer, earns $60 a week.

The Inter-Church Aid Director for the Australian Council of Churches, the Reverend E. Arblaster, said last week: "Conditions are tough for these families we bring in. They have to start from scratch.

"If these people are good enough to be accepted as Australian citizens they should get Government assistance."

Mr Arblaster said that Government assistance to all migrants should be based not on the country of origin but on the migrant's needs.

The World Council of Churches has brought out recently 250 Anglo-Burmese migrants who will have to repay their fare, and some Indian migrants.

Mr Arblaster said the Anglo-Burmese and Indian migrants are in many cases well qualified. Most speak English well, enabling them to get jobs.

"But many migrants have to suffer conditions that, to Australians, seem intolerable," he said.

Unskilled

Mrs Anna Van Ackeran, a social worker with the council, said many of the poor migrants the council sponsored had "a terrible time" here.

To avoid the rent drain, many bought houses and took in two or three other families, she said.

Father Nicholas McSweeney, director of Catholic immigration in Perth, said last week: "It strikes me the Government should consider repayment of the air fares on arrival, or at least look at the house rent situation. In some cases the rent is extortionate.

"We acknowledge the Government has opened the doors on humanitarian grounds. But it's not good enough to say, 'Right. You can come,' then leave them to flounder on their own."

Unassisted migrants come also from Latin America and from communist Europe.

Father John Murphy, director of Catholic immigration in Melbourne, said rental was a big problem for these migrants.

"Most of them are unskilled and can't speak English so they can usually get only laboring-type jobs," he said.

"Many that we have sponsored earn only about $50 to $60 a week and their rent is about $25. Many have to share houses with other families to meet the rent."

Migrants in their thirties and forties found it hard to get a job because of the shortage of work in Australia.

One American finds how dear it is to become an Australian

Where the money went		
		$US
Medical check-up	Robert	200
Medical check-up	Eleanor	75
Smallpox check-up	two children	54
Smallpox shots	$6 ea	24
Police	$3 ea	6
Birth cert	$3 ea	12
Marriage cert	$3	3
Character refs	$5 notary charge	5
Passport photos	16 at 50c ea	8
Passports	$12 ea	24
Drivers' licences	$3 ea	6
Miscellaneous		18
		435
Subsidised passage		500

of policy was that it was too rigid in a changing world. It also overlooked the "real" world pressures exerted by trade, financial and political affiliations. Five-sixths of the world's population was non-white. Nearly half of the world's population was young (under 30) and a sizable proportion of them happened to prefer beards and long hair to the clean-shaven, close-cropped military look. If the door was shut too often, they would batter it down. This was neither to condemn nor to condone such an eventuality, but only to point out its apparent inevitability.

Possibly one of the most significant factors in Australia's development in the past 20 years, has been the immigration scheme. We have found many new resources and capital has been available, but the developments that have occurred could not have taken place without the supply of labour that has come from overseas.

On the whole, the availability of labour has been only just sufficient, and for the development to continue, there can be no doubt that the immigration schemes, which have been so well established, and so well carried on, must continue.

These call for a considerable allocation of resources, for the provision of housing, for the provision of public facilities, and for the provision of all manner of other facilities called for by our modern way of living. Sources of capital will be needed for the more obvious developmental projects, and it is essential that a proper balance be maintained.

—SIR IAN McLENNAN, Managing Director, Broken Hill Proprietory, *National Development Quarterly*, Dec., 1969

An alternative would be to develop flexible policies that modulated the ebb and flow of immigrants according to predicted economic or social needs. This would involve a much more sophisticated level of planning and degree of interstate and federal coordination than existed. Still, with computers, systems analysis, model simulation and electronic communications, it should be possible to predict with reasonable accuracy how many immigrants and what levels of skills and talents would serve the future of Australian interests best. Quotas could then be set on the basis of needs, not race, and reviewed at frequent intervals.

The interests of virtue . . . and the peculiar constitution of our anomalous society, combine in requiring that the agricultural population to be imported into the Colony at the public expense, should consist exclusively of married persons with such unmarried female relatives as they can severally induce to accompany them.
—JOHN DUNMORE LANGE: *Emigration*, 1833

Should this come about, one might assume a "revolving door" (instead of "closed door") policy in which "assisted passage"—where the government paid for or loaned the transportation and moving costs—would have as its complement "assisted passage" out. Under such a policy, people who didn't "work out" or "fit in," or whose term of usefulness had ended, would simply be sent to where they came from, at government expense.

Such a policy had the danger that many "misfits" would be sent home; and it was usually the "misfits" who generated change in society; which lead to the question whether change was either inevitable or desirable. Perhaps for most Australians, the answer might be that changes may be inevitable but they did not have to be drastic, and that they were desirable only to the extent that they contributed to "the quality of life." This latter "quality of life" bit might need some definition, of course, but might not mean increased land development nor industrialization.

"Quality of life" could mean much more extensive and intensive use of automation and mechanization in services and industries, thus maintaining or increasing productivity, while at the same time giving humans more free time to enjoy the things they like to do. To go about it this way would probably involve a highly selective policy of contractual immigration of overseas technologists. Such a policy was already being carried out to a certain extent, but it was mostly industrially oriented. Perhaps it could be more socially oriented.

Another alternative would be to make land areas available on a long-term, fee basis where ethnic groups could work out social experiments on a large scale, using their own people, but purchasing their material needs from the Australians. Such experimental enclaves would greatly diversify and add color to the Australian

experience, while at the same time as sources of service-labour and a ____ voir of talent in the arts, sciences and ____ humanities that would augment the existing Australian ones.

Such communities also could serve as centers for tourism and as linkages for foreign trade.

If the colored people had trouble getting into Australia, the white immigrant who managed to make it didn't have too good a time of it either. Many of the immigrants arrived with very little money, scant understanding of the English language, faced high living costs, and even with Australia's low travel fares, had limited mobility. With these handicaps they only could qualify for menial, low paying jobs, hardly enough to pay the rent and repay the assisted passage fare. They were trapped in poverty and there was not enough money to go back home again.

To men of desperate fortune and the lowest classes of the people, unless they can procure a passage as indented servants, similar to the custom practised of emigrating to America, this part of the world offers no temptation: for it can hardly be supposed that Government will be fond of maintaining them here until they can be settled, and without such support they must starve.
—*Narrative of the Expedition to Botany Bay . . .*, 1789 reprinted in W. Tench: *Sydney's First Four Years*, 1961

Unless they were business executives whose home firm was picking up the tab, the white American fared little better. This seemed to be particularly true of the young American and Canadian families who used up their meager savings to come to Australia to start a new life on the land. It often didn't work out. Farming in Australia was a high risk business. The farming techniques

15

... and Canada did
... stralia; or not for
... expensive acreages
... considerable capital
... ugh reserve capital to
... the long droughts and
... netimes for years. Few
young ... families had these kinds
of resources; if they did have them, they
probably wouldn't have left home in the
first place.

It is indeed melancholy to reflect, that thousands of
British subjects should wander about more like spectres
than beings of flesh and blood, and that hundreds should
die from starvation while our vast Colonies could provide
so abundantly for them. Anxious, however, as a poor man
may be to emigrate to the Australian Colonies with his
family, it is unfortunately, impossible for him to accom-
plish his desire without some assistance.
—CAROLINE CHISHOLM: *The A. B. C. of Colonization,* 1850

This was a tough, hard land, where none
of the "rules" worked. It had filtered out a
tough, hard people. But softies shouldn't
apply; they would never make it. If the land
was any good, it was already being used.
If it wasn't being used, there would be no
way. One contemplated lambs being sold
in Adelaide at two cents each, and since it
took seven cents to get them there, the best
the grazier could do was lose a nickel on
every lamb. It didn't seem to be a very
good business proposition. He had no control of the market price, which was set by
countries thousands of miles away; and no
control of the weather, which drove the
sheep off the land.

The plight of young Americans and
Canadians who emigrated to the big city
areas was not much better. Wages were
low, prices high and opportunities for work
scarce.

THE EMIGRANT'S VISION

As his bark dashed away on the night-shrouded deep,
  And out towards the South he was gazing,
First there passed o'er his spirit a darkness like sleep,
  Then the light of a vision amazing!
As rises the moon, from the white waves afar
Came a goddess, it seemed, of love, wisdom, and war,
And on her bright helmet, encircling a star,
  Behold there was graven "Australia" ...
The swell of his heart, as he rose from his bed,
Broke loud into words on his tongue, and he said—
"Be the home of my hope, then, Australia!"
—CHARLES HARPUR: *Poems,* 1883

Sure, King's Cross in Sydney and the
city of Perth were great fun, while it lasted;
or as long as the money lasted. After that,
washing dishes in backrooms, or making
up other people's beds, or mowing lawns.
Even qualified teachers had a rough time
of it because of archaic bureaucratic regulations that required a certificate that took
two to four more years of work (after
already having graduated from U. S. col-
leges or universities) to be eligible.

Managerial and business types could
become clerks in a bank or other institutions and slowly work their way up through
a highly stratified and ritualized bureaucracy. Husky and energetic young men
could make a good living as miners in the
northern mines, but the work was hard,
brutal and frequently dangerous. Some
could work on the sheep and cattle stations, but most of these were family owned
and run, the work was only seasonal, and
in the outback, the young white immigrant
had to compete with aboriginals who
worked cheap, and knew more about the
land and the care of range stock than the
young white would ever know.

It was not a land of milk and honey, so
glowingly described in the tourist pamphlets, but for the most part a land of
burning sand and rock, or bushfires and
torrential rains. As Mark Twain said, "It is a
land of lies—and all of them are true."

It was also a land with some of the most beautiful scenery in the world. But that part of it was already taken. The rest was only for the strong and brave who could view success with the same steadfast equanimity that they viewed total disaster. It was no place for weaklings, which was why it was so sparsely inhabited.

Looking around, one could see some small patches of darkness. They were not very big, but bothersome just the same.

He came about 10,000 years ago, recently enough in the history of emerging humanity, and he moved in from those outlying northern islands, walking over long-gone land bridges or drifting on logs or rafts to the random sweep of tidal currents, bringing with him his few primitive Stone Age things and that dog of his that was to become the dingo. He did not waken the sleeping land, but he multiplied and wandered and found his own myth in the great quietness, and for thousands of years he, too, was undisturbed. Yet his possession was tenuous, precarious in the huge sprawl of the place, and he was tolerated by the land only because he asked so little of it.
—ROBERT R. GOODMAN/GEORGE JOHNSTON: *The Australians*, Rigby, Ltd., James Place, Adelaide; 1966

Aboriginals to Own Lands

New Australian Policies

Sydney, Australia

In a far-reaching reversal of the previous government's policy, Prime Minister Gough Whitlam has moved to turn over ownership of tribal lands to the indigenous people who have used them for centuries.

Whitlam Friday appointed Justice Albert E. Woodward of Melbourne to head a commission to go into the many problems associated with the land transfers.

Whitlam said the action was a historic one, "demanded by the conscience of the Australian people."

The move goes beyond the previous government's plan to grant the tribes long-term leases. It is a step toward meeting aboriginal demands for outright ownership of lands that the tribes had used for hunting and for their shifting habitations from time immemorial, but lost to white ranchers and mineral developers.

The Whitlam government plans to give the aboriginal groups community titles not only to the lands but also to the mineral and timber rights. Far-reaching economic effects are expected.

The 140,000 aborigines are believed to be the remnants of early migrations from Asia. Some small tribes in Malaysia, Ceylon and India are thought to be related.

Unlike the Indians of North America, the primitive aborigines had little with which to defend themselves against the advancing white settlers in the 19th century. Nevertheless, many were systematically hunted down and killed.

N.Y. Times Service

Men of antiquity were exploring this continent, colonizing more than 30,000 years ago; equipped only sharp-edged stones and a larger brain than the ancestor, Australopithecine, these incredible men spr[ead] across the world on foot and by water to face the harsh facts and resources of this land. They not only survived a dreadful ice age but fashioned a culture and social structure of beauty and appeal.
—LENNARD BICKEL: "An Unwritten Page Out of the Past," *The Australian*, Dec. 22, 1971

He invented no wall or wheel, built no dwellings, planted no crops, learnt no writing, fathered no civilization. He had little sense of future and he made no effort to find wealth or to develop sustenance from the soil under his calloused nomadic feet. What he did develop was the richest of primitive arts and mythology of his own —a complicated "Black Genesis," a "dreaming time" and pattern of life, a strange and rigid pastiche of giants and spirits, of totem and fetish, that only now is capturing the more sophisticated imaginations of our contemporary scholars and poets.
—ROBERT R. GOODMAN/GEORGE JOHNSTON: *The Australians*, Rigby, Ltd., James Place, Adelaide, 1966

Theoretically, any black qualifies for accommodation at Ammonguna, the reserve nearest Alice Springs. And yet the quaint stage-one housing, built of those same aluminum strips that serve for instant runways in Vietnam, is mostly empty, except for the flies gathering on the dirt on the walls. Peering through an unglazed window into the single tiny tin room, you yearn again for the breezes of the creek bed where you can get your gear off and roll in the warm red sand when the mood takes you . . .
—GERMAINE GREER: "Greer of the Inland," *The Review*, March 4-10, 1972

Silence ruled this land. Out of silence, mystery comes, and magic and the delicate awareness of unreasoning things. The black man learned from it, having no other teacher . . . Thought made man one with his environment . . . Eternity was ever-present to him; past and future interwoven with his own life by legend and unvarying tradition, so that all time was frame for his mortality and contentment his heritage.
—ELEANOR DARK: *The Timeless Land*, London, 1942

By 1973, there were only 40,000 full-blooded aborigines left (about 1 percent of the total population) and about 120,000 half-breeds, who were perhaps the most unfortunate of all the tragic figures in this play, because they were unaccepted in either of the two worlds available to them.

The love of these people for their land was equally apparent. It is far more than their food-provider or a series of places of pleasant memories. Their spirit comes from the land and enters the body of their mother. Upon death, the spirit returns to the land.
—FRANCES PURCELL: *The Sunday Australian*, Dec. 5, 1971

"The First Kangaroo" from *Dreamtime*, by Ainslie Roberts. (From the collection of Sir Robert G. Menzies.)

Who are these shy people with shiny black skins, thick lips, flat noses and skinny legs? Precise knowledge of their origin is lacking . . . It seems most likely that the Australoid race, of which the aborigines are representative and which conforms with none of the world's three main racial groups, originated many thousands of years ago in the islands north of Australia, particularly Java. These hunters and food gatherers probably moved slowly north to Malaya and India, south to New Guinea (where they developed into a new racial sub-group), and then to Australia. Here, undisturbed for many centuries, they preserved their original racial type, which had remained substantially unchanged. From their first landings on Cape York and elsewhere in the north, they spread up and down the coast and by way of the great river system, across the continent.
—REVEREND HUBERT TEMME, *The Aborigines of Australia,* 1872.

The myths of the Australian aborigines, which deal with the creation of their universe and the establishment of the rules of human behavior that all must follow, are accepted as revelations of absolute truth and are the foundations of their social and secular and ceremonial life. The reenactment of these beliefs in the ceremonial grounds provides the actors with a deep religious experience comparable to that of a practicing Catholic taking part in the Mass.

These myths describe how, before creation times, the uncreated and eternal earth had always existed as a large flat disc floating in space. Its uninhabited surface was a vast featureless plain, extending unbroken to the horizon. No hills or watercourses broke its monotonous surface, no trees or grass covered its nakedness, nor did the calls of birds or animals disturb its quiet. It was a dead, silent world. Yet slumbering beneath that monotonous surface, were indeterminate forms of life that would even-

"Tirlat and the Flowers of Blood," from *Dreamtime*. (From the collection of Mrs. E. Stacy.)

tually transform the forbidding landscape into the world as the aborigines knew it today.

As the ages passed, these mythical beings began to emerge from beneath the plain and to wander haphazardly over its surface . . .

—CHARLES P. MOUNTFORD, from the introduction to *The First Sunrise*, Illustrated by Ainslie Roberts, Rigby, Ltd., Adelaide, 1971

Meanwhile, their art was being exploited by white Australians who, until quite recently, had little art of their own. The aboriginal art was mostly reproduced in Japan and sold to credulous Americans and Britishers in tourist traps in Sydney and Melbourne. The aborigines got nothing out of this, either.

The aboriginal names remained on the land that was no longer theirs. More importantly, they entered the white man's mind at night, giving him at best, bad dreams; at worst, nightmares. Numerically small as they are, the aborigines' psychic emanations continued to be a powerful influence on the continent. Their "dreamtime" was as potent as any atomic bomb that the white man, in his own nightmare, could conjure up.

"Goolagaya and the White Dingo," from *Dreamtime*.
(From the collection of Mrs. R. W. LeMessurier.)

ALCHERINGA
The hallowing of the land received a new extension when it was linked with the aboriginal religion as the sacred place of the tribe, associated with the great creative powers of the universe, made holy by spirits of the Dream Time. Indeed, place and spirit are so interwoven that they can be merged into one another since, as Dr. Stanner points out, "A black fellow may call his totem, or the place from which his spirit came, his Dreaming." For centuries its inhabitants had regarded the land as holy, inspiring awe and reverence, a source of spiritual strength flowing to the worshipper.
—T. INGLIS MOORE: *Social Patterns in Australian Literature*, Angus and Robertson, Pty., Ltd., Sydney, 1971

One liked to think that this black influence would continue, and perhaps to grow. It was Australia's richest cultural heritage. Looking about, gazing down the corridors, one could see some light at the end of the tunnel, faint as that light might be. There had been one aborigine elected to Parliament. One had even written and published a book—but that was in another room— New Guinea. In that room, breech clothed aborigines were monitoring highly sophisticated, Japanese designed and built electric consoles at a plywood plant in the

"Wyungare and the Avenging Fire," from *The First Sunrise*, by Ainslie Roberts and Charles P. Mountford, Rigby, Ltd., Adelaide, 1971. (From the collection of Whaler's Inn, Rosetta Bay.)

Central Highlands. These were the same people who were "too dumb" to be given more than a third grade education.

But all was not lost.

A famous aboriginal artist in Central Australia was given a house by well-meaning white friends. He lived in it one week and then sold the roof to a close friend. The house was never occupied again. In fact, an aborigine once said to me, "Why should I live in a house? A white man puts up four walls to keep the weather out, knocks holes in the walls to let the weather in, covers the holes up with glass to keep the weather out and then shoves the windows up to let the weather in. He doesn't know what he wants. Why should I follow him?"
—REVEREND HUBERT TEMME: *The Aborigines of Australia*

There were some faint, but perceptible stirrings. You had to have sharp eyes to see them, but they lurked in the corners of the room. Too late for Tasmania; the last aborigine died in 1889. But still not too late for the rest of Australia nor New Guinea. Perhaps not too late.

The Aborigine is very close to emerging from his former shadowy status of nonperson; as a positive member of society he will be a new dynamic in the development of an Australian nation.
But if the Government is going to fulfill its role of encouraging this development, it must surely start from the premise—which in some quarters today is deemed rather eccentric—that people are often more important than economic development.
—*The Australian Financial Review*, Jan. 25, 1972

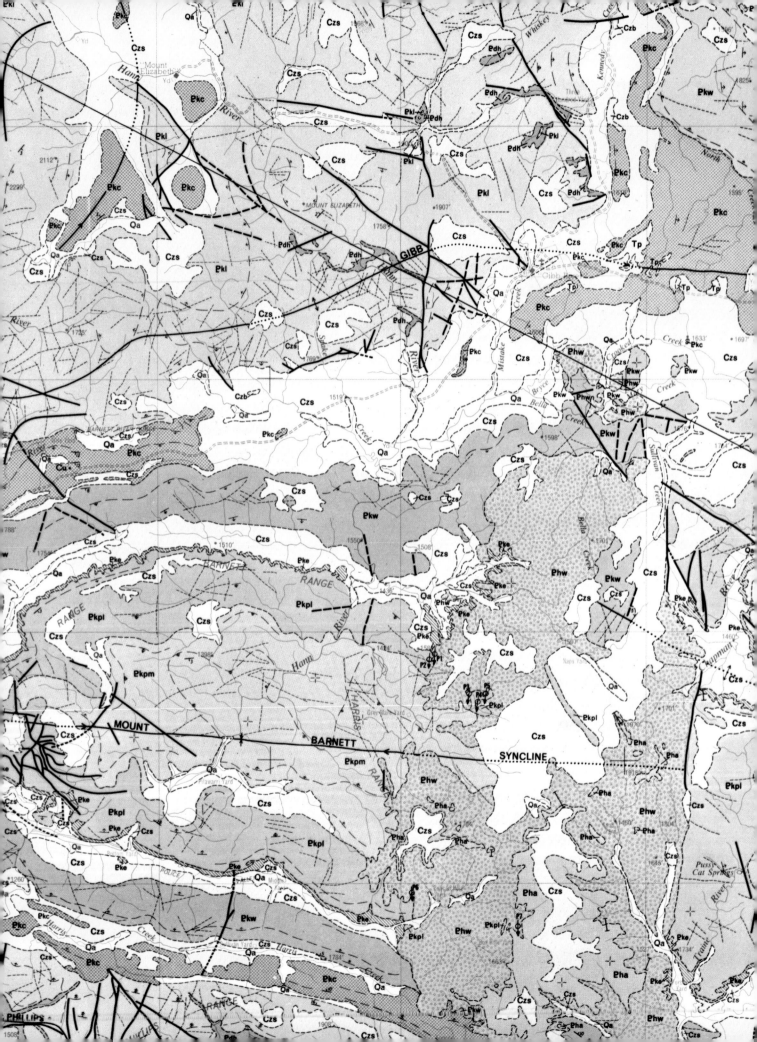

As one walked from room to room, one felt there was a sort of collective consciousness in them; a colony of minds, derived from many genetic strains, from many acculturations. It was—this collective consciousness—only one's own mind. What, then, should this mind think? Australia had been called "the mindless continent," yet when one looked it over, there obviously was a mind there.

There did seem to be a pattern. One part of it was to work as little as possible in order to have as many holidays as possible.

Where did that part of the pattern come from?

It might have been from the convict colony days. Everyone had to work all week long to build meaningless forts against non-existent enemies.

How is the problem of the greatest possible amount of happiness for the greatest number to be affected?
I will tell you. By regulating the number of hours a man shall work in a day, sufficient to feed, clothe and educate the population, and with a due regard to the advantages in which we should share by the introduction of labour-saving machines, we should also prevent the pernicious tendency to over-production, which has too often proved disastrous to many of the great manufacturing centres of the world . . .
—CHARLES JARDINE DON: (c) 1860, from W. E. Murphy: *History of the Eight Hours' Movement*, Vol. 1, 1896

Look upon the toiling millions of the world, who lay the foundations of all physical, intellectual and moral prosperity. What scheme should be left untried to raise up the industrial masses of this and every other country? And what scheme stands so great a chance of success as the Eight Hours' Movement?
— W. E. MURPHY: *History of the Eight Hours' Movement*, Vol. 1, 1896

The backlash of 200 years was a sort of hedonism. Looking forward, could such a society withstand the economic competition of the Japanese, the Chinese, the Germans, the Russians and the Americans?

Why not? Those other societies were wearing themselves out producing things they didn't need, to sell to others who did not want them. Could there not be a life-style that gave people at least the option of producing only the necessities for survival, and then just enjoy life in their own way? As long as what they did did not hurt anyone else.

Now, this was an attractive proposition, but not a very realistic one.

Hedonistic or not, they were very materialistic people. They led, largely, a suburban life; perhaps the most uneconomic way of life yet invented by humans. Everyone's dream appeared to be the ownership of a small house on a little bit of land, surrounded by a fence.

The molecular unit of sprawl is the five-roomed house. As architect and critic Robin Boyd has written: "The Australian town-dweller spent a century in the acquisition of his toy: an emasculated garden, a five-roomed cottage of his very own, different from its neighbours by a minor contortion of a window or porch—its difference significant to no one but himself. He skimped and saved for it, and fought two World Wars, with it figuring prominently in the back of his mind. Whenever an Australian boy spoke to an Australian girl of marriage, he meant, and she understood him to mean, a life in a five-roomed house."
—ROBIN BOYD: *The Australian Ugliness*, F. W. Cheshire 1960.

This was, rather obviously, an extension of the English way of thinking.

Now, if the Australian population were to remain relatively stable, then the suburban system might turn out to be workable. If the population increased substantially by the year 2000, then some other system would have to be created; perhaps model cities or cluster cities.

But one still had to deal with a mind that was moulded in the 19th Century tradition, and whether that mind might change to adapt to a post-industrial, technological society was doubtful.

The "set" of the Australian mind tended toward conservatism and the preservation of past patterns.

But we are in a curious state of mind in these colonies. The land is young, the people are all young, their experience is only a few years' date, but the association and sympathies of the majority now living are with old times, and men and things at home. To this latter cause we must attribute the constant tendency to imitate and "reproduce" the old country as much as possible. This tendency, in many respects, has amounted to a morbid prejudice, an absurdity, and an injury. It is a fact that, during the last summer, gentlemen for the first time adopted a rational costume, suited to the hottest days, and (no doubt with dogged reluctance and stupid hesitations) laid aside their hot cloth clothing, glaring patent-leather boots, and feverish black hats.
—R. H. HORNE: *Australian Facts and Prospects*, 1859

Nearly all the pressures of the outside world pointed in the opposite direction.

Whether these vectors would converge or diverge was an open question. But, in either case, the end result would be much the same. Perhaps among the people of the world, only the Australians could plan to build an affluent society; a life that was more leisure than work; more fun and games than dull bureaucratic days wasted in little rooms. Would the Australian mind accept the challenge and show the world the way, or would it cling to a system of repetitive worldwide error?

What, then, appeared to be unique in the Australian mind (assuming, again, a sort of collective consciousness)?

The three main characteristics of the native Australian appear to be the following:
1. An inordinate love of field sports.
2. A very decided disinclination to recognize the authority of parents and superiors.
3. A grievous dislike to mental effort. . . .
Young Australia's third defect of character I have described as 'a grievous dislike to mental effort'. Is it not exceedingly strange that, whilst the most eager interest is manifested in the doings of the Australian cricketers in England, the utmost indifference is shown towards the triumphs of Australian genius in other and more enobling spheres?. . . Trickett, the rower, and Murdoch, the cricketer, who achieve nothing more than what an ignorant South-sea islander could do if he wished, are to be cheered and lauded, their portraits submitted for our admiration, and their glorious deeds enthusiastically described in the newspapers, whilst men of brains are to be treated with cold neglect.
— JAMES F. HOGAN: "The Coming Australian," *Hogan Vic. Review*, 1880

Many people have said that Australians are much like the people in the United States. Both countries went through the same ritual—"discovery," exploration, the emigration from the coastal cities toward the interior, the gold rush, Chinese coolie labor, urbanization, an increasingly growing nonproductive bureaucracy, depression, recession and environmental pollution and destruction. All of the cliches in the history books. And some still say that Australia is the "U. S. A. revisited," some 100 years ago. Which, of course simply is not true. It was hard to see in what way the Australians were lagging behind the Americans.

And there most certainly appeared to be a difference between the Australian mind and the American mind, even though both started in much the same way and followed the same general course.

Now, in this moment of reflection, was it possible to describe the difference, or to track down how it came about? Or was it really just a time-lag?

One would start with the similarities. To begin with, it was for North Europeans a case of being a "stranger in a strange land."

Just as when Ben Franklin, and others, sent back from the American colonies strange artifacts, flora and fauna, and they were rejected by the scientific "authorities" as "preposterous."

The trees were different, the birds were different, the insects were different, colour was different, the light was different, the very scale of the landscape was different, sounds were different. The flowers, though violently chromatic and prodigal in variety, were without scent and strangely bristly. There was a profusion of insects of the oddest types and an extraordinary range of reptiles that seemed to have survived from some long lost world. The birds were bewildering, the fish improbable, the animals absurd. The aborigines seemed hardly to belong to a human species. The ironhard eucalyptus trees defied axe and adze and auger. The soil had no affinity for the plough; indeed it must have laughed to feel the puny tickle of those first picks and shovels. And every dawn greeted the settlers with the crazed cackle of the kookaburra as if the land was mocking its reluctant invaders. It was as though the old continent could have thrown them all off with one brief shrug of its huge shoulders.
— ROBERT R. GOODMAN & GEORGE JOHNSTON: *The Australians*, Rigby Ltd., James Place, Adelaide, 1966

The white Western Europeans, and most particularly those in the British Isles, could not help but believe they were the center of the civilized world, and already, through Church and King, had all the right answers. This strange anomaly ran through the psychic background of both the Americans and the Australians. It was a form of parental rejection from the Motherland. Given a strange environment, both colonial people tried to change it to be as much like dear old England (or Scotland and Ireland) as possible.

"I have striven to reproduce our English life as far as possible," said William with pride and complacency. "I think it is the duty of every Englishman to reproduce English conditions as far as possible wherever he may be. The man who does not is, I don't scruple to say it, a renegade.... What finer thing can he do for Australia than make it another England? ... Ours is a race of empire-builders because no Englishman worthy of the name ever yields to climate or environment."
—T. INGLIS MOORE, *Social Patterns in Australian Literature*, Angus and Robertson, Pty., Ltd., Sydney, 1971

In the history of both countries, it was felt that the planting of a sovereign flag somehow established ownership. It was still believed in both countries that the white man owned the land because he was the first to plant a flag there. At one time, of course, the Spaniards, Portuguese, French and Germans believed the same thing; in every case, the new colonies were established by weaponry and not morality.

In both America and Australia it was still believed that the white man "owned" the land, whatever *that* might mean. If might made right, then that was it.

This "set" of the mind, the grain direction, was an important input because it determined the patterns for the handling of the indigenous cultures, how the land and its native animals and vegetables were to be treated, a militant posture in the world protecting land ownership (a "territorial imperative" if you like) and, of course, a society built solidly on the ownership of land and artifacts and a cult for protecting them.

It is in Australia that the battle against Nature's brutal laws will be fought out; it is here in Australia that human society will develop itself, and that the yet-unanswered riddles of the Sphinx will be finally solved.
—WILLIAM LANE: *The Boomerang*, Nov. 19, 1887

The Yin and Yang of the Australian mind was the brightness it assumed for its future and the dark pessimism it felt for its past. It hovered like a moth between the kerosene lamp and the darkness out back.

Its main causes were the unpredictable onslaught of drought, flood and fire, the struggle with an arid and recalcitrant land, the loneliness of a harsh bush life, and the tragic death of explorers. Like the realism with which it is interlinked, it also had the convict system as a historical determinant. In the literature, the social realists became professional specialists in sombreness as they concentrated on the ills of society.
—T. INGLIS MOORE: *Social Patterns in Australian Literature*, Angus and Robertson, Pty., Ltd., Sydney, 1971

There was something between the glitter of its city lights and the brooding waiting darkness of the bush and its people. It hovered there but did not as yet know which way to go. Except, being phototropic, toward the light.

The CORNSTALK: Man of the To-Day expanding and extending into the To-Morrow's Homo-Ultimate: inheriting the World within his Blood and Brawn and Brain and parting with his Birthright only with the Mooning of the Earth;
I see and sing
The Mob of Millions who compose
The CORNSTALK: mythic Man: supposititious personality: ideal individuality: the counterfeit presentment of a multitide in one;
The Mob of Millions: each a Leaf upon the Man-branch of the Zoologic Tree: the universal Yggdrasill;
The Mob of Millions: each an Iliad: an actual epitome of all:
a sum organic of the world!
—FRANK COWAN: "The Cornstalk: Mythic Man," *Australia: A Charcoal Sketch*, 1886

One thought about this for a moment or maybe two hundred years and decided it didn't make any difference—back to the dark or forward to the light. Because, being blind with the rays of time, one couldn't tell the difference anyway. But blind in a special sense; that darkness and light were essentially the same. Somewhere in between—Aristotle's excluded middle, if one liked—there could be an accommodation. Color it grey. But among the large countries, only Australia had the option to choose. The rest were all on an easily predictable, iron-railed, downhill course to oblivion.

The question inevitably arose; was grey the "right" color? Middle-of-the-roadism was at least one of the courses still open; a model perhaps, for the "Third World." Was someone building a "Fourth World"? One did not know, and as a matter of fact, did not care. The "Third World" would be enough during one's time here.

"She'll be right, mate," was often used by Americans, and some Australians, as a derogatory expression. But there was something very optimistic in the phrase, too. "Give 'er a go" could apply appropriately to everything from starting a new mine or a store, or wandering off into the bush, to betting on fancy New Zealand horses at the tracks; to trying "the big 'un'" on the Queensland surf. "Two-up" was still a popular game at Broken Hill and at the Canberra Club. Slot machines went great in Queanbeyan. The N.S.W. lottery helped to build the Sydney Opera House.

One can bet on anything in Australia; but "better bet that you're wrong." It's that kind of country.

Another important idea, with enormous potential for the future, was that the working man—in mines, on stations, in factories, even in offices—was not the subordinate of his boss, but at least equal to him. His efforts—the working man's—supported the boss; not the other way around.

An essential part of the Australian mind was an incorrigible optimism concerning the future. In part, this psychological euphoria may have stemmed from ingrained beliefs; that open land represented opportunity; that global isolation gave military immunity; that inexhaustible resources were just waiting for someone to stumble upon them, and that the capital and labor to develop them profitably would be furnished by overseas sources. Like all human attitudes, these were partly right and partly wrong, but the balance, over time, seemed somewhat to favor the "right"

What is the dominant note of
Australian scenery? That which is
the dominant note of Edgar Allen
Poe's poetry — Weird Melancholy
. . . The Australian forests are
funereal, secret, stern. Their
solitude is desolation. They seem to
stifle in their black gorges a story
of sullen despair.
MARCUS CLARKE, "Australian Scenery"
from the preface to Gordon's poems, *The
Marcus Clark Memorial Volume*
(Melbourne 1884), pp. 114-15

Sir J. Longstaff
Gippsland, Sunday Night
Feb. 20, 1898

side. Inevitably, this spirit of optimism was transferred to the political field:

In short, taking into account the vast galaxy of isles to the eastward and northward of Australia, in addition to the extensive coasts of this great continental island itself, I question whether even the United States of America will have a more extensive field of political power and of moral influence to expatiate over than will one day acknowledge the sovereignty of the United Provinces of Australia.
—JOHN DUNMORE LANG: "The Sovereignty of the United Provinces of Australia," *The Coming Event*, 1850

Despite long droughts and torrential rains and its continental isolation from "civilized" countries, one persisted in believing that everything would come out right in the end, whatever that end might be.

This was at the basis of the gambling instinct—try her enough times and she'll be right—whether in farming, or raising sheep and cattle, or exploring that ridge of rock for metals just once more. There had to be gold there. Or something.

Well, if one wanted to live at all, this was not a bad mood to be in. And, for the Australians most of them had so far made it. They had a great deal of pride in themselves, and confidence in their destiny.

From all the Negatives of the sepulchral No-Man's-Land, the Never-Never Country, to the Positives of Queensland, New South Wales, Victoria, Australia South, Australia West—collectively,
The Hand Five-fingered of the Mistress of the Seas that grasps the Grand Prize of the Southern World;
The Paw Five-taloned of the Lion of the North that takes the Lion's Share of the Huge Carcass of South;
The YANKEELAND beneath the Southern Cross;
Among the Nations of the Earth, a Nation of Enlightment, the blazon of whose glorious banner has not been an empty boast, ADVANCE!
—FRANK COWAN: *Australia: a Charcoal-Sketch*, 1886

Whenever one bet on a horse race, or the dogs or the mining stocks, there was an inevitable feeling of optimism about the future. One would lose a few times, sure,

but in the end, she'd be right. Would the Australians gamble on the year 2000 in the same incorrigible way? One thought it likely that they would.

The present actors will soon disappear from the stage. Already, those whom we knew so well in the early days of the Constitution we know no more. A new generation is close upon us; the many will know no other land than fair Australia. They will bring, let us hope, with the tie of nativity, more ample stores of knowledge, nobler capacities for patriotic service, and an imperishable love of freedom and justice. Standing before the unlifted veil, let the meanest of us breathe a fervent prayer, that the Almighty may guide the young commonwealth on the high-road of her starry future, that her people may be abundantly blessed within these encompassing seas of peace, and that their influence beyond may be a blessing to all mankind.
—HENRY PARKES: *Fifty Years in the Making of Australian History*, 1892

Australia, advancing with rapid wing'd stride,
Shall plant among nations her banners in pride:
The yoke of dependence aside she will cast,
To build on the ruins the wrecks of the Past.
—HENRY KENDALL: *Australian Home Companion and Band of Hope Journal*, Nov. 5, 1859

The concept of "freedom," at least for white settlers, was intrinsic to the Australian mind. First it was expressed as opposition to the British guards—some convicts ran away into the bush and some of them made it. Some of the guards also escaped to the bush, and some of *them* made it, too. Together the escapees, guards and convicts alike, if they survived the bush, became the national heroes.

Then sing the Tree of Liberty,
  And the men who shall defend
Its glorious future righteously
  For this all-glorious end—
That happiness all men to bless
  Out with its growth may grow—
Our Southern Tree of Liberty
  Shall flourish even so!
—CHARLES HARPUR: "On, ye Red Republicans," *The Bushrangers . . . and Other Poems*, 1853

Because they were all—guards and convicts—imprisoned in their own way, the mere idea of freedom was a compulsion that overrode all feelings of personal safety or even survival. *Anything* would be better than this! And so they went, to establish the only long-lasting, genuine (even if mythological) characteristic of the white Australian: the image of the Bushman.

> The melancholy of the bush is an influence which, once thoroughly established, is never shaken off. Yet the bush is the heart of the country, the real Australian Australia, and it is with the Bushman that the final fate of the nation and race will lie. The West made and carried through the Secession War in America. It saved the Union by giving it not only a Western president and a Western general, but the only troops who could crush the genius and passion of the South. For the West was the real American America, the characteristic type of that new democracy. Well, there is but one absolutely new and characteristic type in Australia, and that type is the Bushman.
> —FRANCIS ADAMS: *The Labour Movement in Australia*, (1891), Sun Books, Melbourne, 1968

Much of the hard talk and roughness of the pubs in Sydney and Melbourne and other metropolitan centers, such as Perth

THE AUSTRALIAN
FINANCIAL REVIEW
FRIDAY, MARCH 17, 1972
Sydney: Melbourne:
Box 506, GPO, 2001.   392 Little Collins St, 3000.

Any intellectual can play

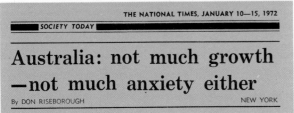

THE NATIONAL TIMES, JANUARY 10—15, 1972
SOCIETY TODAY

Australia: not much growth —not much anxiety either

By DON RISEBOROUGH   NEW YORK

and Adelaide, stems from the mythic image of the Bushman, and the desire to emulate it. The one characteristic that the Bushmen shared—be they escapees, renegades, "no hopers," misfits, ne'er-do-wells, emigres—was the sense of freedom and a vision of liberty.

The price of freedom is loneliness; the price of liberty is danger. The Bushman paid both prices with a deep melancholy; what Joseph Conrad in another continent at another time called, "The Heart of Darkness." It runs throughout the "outback" bush ballads and poetry and music; graffiti on journalistic outhouse walls. These were voices crying out in terror in their vast loneliness; they died, unechoed in the thousand-mile darkness. The lack of answering voices produced what Edgar Allen Poe called "The Weird Melancholy."

This darkness in the heart of the flower children, who were best described by H. G. Wells in the "Time Machine," permeates even the glass and aluminum cenotaphs on Collins Street in Melbourne; even the pubs and the post-work happy hour; even the backyard, suburban, eucalyptus leaf barbecue.

> Few places can show so strange a mixture, and yet so complete a "fusion," of the heterogeneous materials of its society as "the Bush" of Australia. It is curious to see men differing so entirely in birth, education and habits, and in their whole moral and intellectual nature, thrown into such close contact, united common interests, engaged under circumstances of perfect equality in the same pursuits.
> —H. W. HAYGARTH: *Recollections of Bush Life in Australia During a Residence of Eight Years in the Interior* (London, 1848)

It was important to think about, when considering the future of the Land of Oz (as in Australia) because this not wholly hidden pessimism, born of the burning desire for freedom and liberty, would give a dark tone to many of the decisions the people of Australia would have to make as they entered the 21st Century.

A part of the vector would be determined by the call of the wild, even if the individuals at Canberra had never experienced it themselves. But it was there; the night of the day of these tough-talking Bushmen, inspired fun-loving gamblers on the edge of the world.

Later on, the earlier desire to escape "authority" and the bureaucratic "establishment" expressed itself in the form of a very mild-mannered revolt against the autocracy of the mother country. It led to independence, of a sort.

> . . . If there is any part of the habitable globe, where men are free, it is Australia. In regard to the supreme authority of Government, it is no figure of speech to say that we Australians are held to the Empire by a golden link. It could not be of lighter weight or of more intrinsic value. The British tie gives us a standing in the world, which is illumined by all the glory of the fatherland and which carries in its very fibre the heroic greatness of our race.
> —HENRY PARKES: "No Other Land Than Fair Australia," *Fifty Years in the Making of Australian History*, 1892

Today, that same desire for freedom expressed itself as opposition to what it conceived to be business bureaucracy of the technologically "advanced" countries; mostly the United States, Western Europe and Japan. It was, in some respects, a child's revolt against parental control.

> We do not want to be a nation such as the old nations are; we do not want a worthless king, a parasitic aristocracy and a plundering hierarchy rioting above, with a seething mass of poverty-stricken humanity struggling below; we do not want to be a continent-full of warring tribes; we do not want to be a sheep-run and a cane-plantation and a cattle-station, growing beef and mutton and sugar for an antipodean market; nor while we encourage enterprise of Capital do we want to so neglect the just claims of Labour that the coming nation will be slain at its birth by bitter social war. No programme can be complete which does not embrace proposals for the surmounting of these difficulties which separate the state we have from the state we would like to have.
> —WILLIAM LANE: *Boomerang*, Sept. 1, 1888

There appeared to be, underlying the pragmatism, a dream there. The dream was of a virtually classless society. It seemed to have been a kind of pleasant dream, for pleasant people, and perhaps the dream had not ended yet. At least it seemed worth examining, because much of the Australian attitude appeared to be based upon it. (One is not saying that the Australians had achieved a classless society, anymore than one could say that the United States had achieved a democracy. One simply wanted to explore the concept of a classless society because it probably was the central human dilemma of an increasingly crowded world.) A solution *could* come from the Australians.

A classless society would be based on the almost unexamined assumption that all men are created equal. As a concept, it seemed patently absurd. It had been the dream of Abraham Lincoln and of Karl Marx; but a dream only. In its practical applications, it had not worked out very well for the Americans nor the Russians nor the Chinese.

Why hadn't it worked out? For one thing, there appeared to be no biological, cultural nor geographic basis to believe that all people were born equal. It was a mighty ideal and a useful political statement, but when examined, it did not seem to have any more substance than a ghost.

In Australia, the ghost still walked. In its wake bobbled some rather curious phenomena. For starters, there were "mateship," anti-intellectualism, and a form of pseudo-socialism; the latter both accepting and rejecting established authority.

The whole concept of mateship may have come from the colonial convicts and the men of the Outback. Whatever its origin, mateship implied that one person would help another. Strenuous competitors in their rough sports, the Australians nevertheless helped each other along the dusty trail or through the floods of the Big Wet, whenever help was needed.

Mateship was a sort of marriage, without the sexual connotations; a marriage of shared dangers during the day, meeting at the pub after, and sharing the lonesome billy-can at night.

So it was less from social circumstance that the principles of "mateship" sprang, than from those "brute facts of Australian geography." Mateship, that peculiarly Australian sub-philosophy, was a product of the immense distance and utter loneliness of the "bush," of the stupefying scale of space and emptiness and the raw nature in which man had to contend for survival. From these brute facts came the strong sense of social solidarity, the ingrained sense of the rights of the individual with its rigid rule that every man was entitled to a "fair go." For in such a country, the enormity was too much not to be shared.
—ROBERT B. GOODMAN and GEORGE JOHNSTON: *The Australians*, Rigby Ltd., Adelaide, 1966

In mateship, there was a great portent for the future, because once a society learned that people survive by helping each other, leaving competition to sports and game playing, then there was at least a chance for global human survival. One could even conceive of Australian mateship being extended to other countries and even to people of differently colored skins and quite different cultures.

It was at least an alternative future that the extension of mateship could take, and possibly could determine the social nature of the 21st Century.

There were other directions. There could be a return to a sort of isolationism in which only the white Australians clung together. But that seemed an unlikely course. In an increasingly crowded world, with the advances in transportation and communication technology, the Australians could be isolated no more.

The Australian pub, with its late afternoon fraternity, might in the end turn out to be the most effective weapon for peace that Australia had or could produce. A weapon for peace—the world needed it. Perhaps the Australians alone had the background, experience, ability and opportunity to develop it.

The ingredients that mixed together to create mateship also helped to create a mild sort of anti-intellectualism. This was not the Hitlerian book-burning kind, but more a distrust of the formally educated classes who usually ended up running things.

Utterly devoid of all intellectual and spiritual significance, their conscious social life is either intolerably common or intolerably pretentious. You choose between kindly, hospitable folk who have never got beyond parochialism and the primal appetites, and mincing, mouthing nonenities, aping English "society" at second hand.
—FRANCIS ADAMS: *The Labour Movement in Australia*, 1891

Nearly fifty years later, the statement, or accusation, or whatever it was, still ran strong.

> This country of great distances does not necessarily breed great minds. It tends, on the contrary, to breed narrow ones . . . I have met throughout Australia men who were as well-informed and as imaginative as any one could wish for; but they are not typical. A great many of their countrymen made me feel that I was talking to precociously alert and self-satisfied children; and that I was an old, old man.
> —THOMAS WOOD: *Cobbers,* Melbourne, 1948

Run the tape for another twenty years. One heard:

> Throughout the world the basis of material prosperity in the future is likely to lie, for the first time in history, with clever, educated people. The need to build up a certain kind of cleverness will cause great social tensions in all industrialized countries; but especially in Australia, where cleverness can be considered un-Australian.
> —DONALD HORNE: *The Lucky Country,* Penguin Books, Pty., Ltd., Adelaide, 1964

Two strange counter-currents were that the Australians turned out to have the highest readership of books and periodicals per capita of any nation on earth, and that they had more Nobel prize winners, based on the population, than any other country, too. This was a strange sort of thing to have happen, but it did.

One wondered why. It was something like an aboriginal in the bush, trying to catch a goanna for dinner; one might track it down. In the early days, culture depended largely on the balladeer, the wanderer, the man from the coast who

Science standing

Sir — Professor W. P. Rogers correctly complains about the "growing distaste for science as a means of tackling environmental problems" ("Advertiser," 18/1/72). But nowhere in the report of his address to the Summer School of Environmental Studies is there any discussion of how this anti-science counter-culture has arisen.

As a scientist who feels that environmental problems must be approached by a combination of rational discussion and political action, and, who has learnt here the hard way what to expect of many of one's fellow scientists when a scientist needs to publicise an environmental error, I have come to the conclusion that scientists themselves are to a considerable extent responsible for the present anti-science trend.

Anti-science trend 'disturbing'

There were disturbing signs of a growing distaste for science as a means of tackling environmental problems, an Adelaide academic said last night.

34

carried his news and his stories in his mind, just as he carried his provisions for the long trip outback in his tucker bag for camping by the billabong. Books and book-learning were relatively rare and, in any event, had little meaning in that context. It was much as early England may have been.

Another input to anti-intellectualism, and to anti-establishment as well, may have been the convict legend or mythos, or what you will. Most, if not all, of the convicts were quite ordinary people from the lower economic classes, who had been convicted under the laws of their time (for stealing a loaf of bread, perhaps), but mostly their crime was that they were poor. And, under the English system, only the rich were educated. And they ran the camps. Thus, for most of the convicts, education and punishment were equated. The establishment meant the educated class, and both were equated with the abuse of authority over the poor. The poor were the people who worked for a living; the educated and/or titled rich did not.

This seemed an important consideration for the future, because the majority of the people would probably reject any new idea or concept except for the purely technological, on the grounds that the Establishment was trying to put something over on them.

Whatever the psychological causes, one could trace a sort of linear progression— sea-dog, to convict, to Bushman, to mateship, to anti-intellectualism and its natural offspring—anti-Establishment. The grandchild was the trade union movement.

The bush ideal of mateship found its expression in the "new unions" of the bushworkers—particularly the Shearers' Union, whose first president was W. G. Spence. Writing later in his memoirs (Australia's Awakening), Spence declared that unionists have starved rather than accept work under other conditions. Hundreds of men have worn their boots and clothes to tatters seeking work upon Union terms; and not finding it, have gone without for a year—remaining penniless, but independent and felt that they had not degraded themselves . . . Men imbued with such a spirit put the cause above personal self-interest. They need no prompting—no exciting by fiery orators— but stood loyal to principle, no matter what the consequences might be. Rough and unpolished many of them may be; but manly, true, and "white" all the time and the movement owes them much.

We have been placed at the very apex of the pyramid of created things. We have, by the exercise of our superior intelligence been able to control many of the forces of Nature and utilize them for our own good. We have been able, to a greater degree than any of the lower forms of life, to take advantage of co-operation, or of forming alliances for mutual benefit. In this great movement called "Trades Unionism" or the "Labour Movement" . . . we and the same evolutionary spirit had been at work . . . You cannot expect the working classes—especially those who are crushed most low—to be so polished and nice as those who have nothing to do but study how to be polished and nice. These evils are directly attributable to that condition of society which it has set up to be over itself . . .

—W. G. SPENCE:
1892

The trade union movement in Australia was a very powerful influence. It established not only working hours and conditions, but welfare and social security policy, tariff protection and through the Arbitration Commission a system of accommodation between the opposed forces. It also established a political party that vies for power with the Establishment party.

In Australia . . . the working class has been the class contributing most to the shaping of social patterns. Thus, some of the differences between the Australian and the American outlooks may perhaps be reasonably traced back to the difference between the psychology of the working class and that of the lower middle class.
—T. INGLIS MOORE: Social Patterns in Australian Literature, Angus and Robertson, Pty., Ltd., Sydney, 1971

35

But the question did arise whether this influence would last until the year 2000. There was always the possibility that union leadership might join forces with big business and leave the workingman out in the cold. The workingman did have at least one ace in the hole. He could just refuse to show up for work; or go "smoko" for awhile and the epidemic of work stoppages over the years seemed to indicate that this was the direction the trade unionists might take.

It was a dangerous course to steer, like making it through one of the passes of the Barrier Reef without a navigation chart. The bosses didn't produce much except bureaucracy and paperwork.

If he, the beer guzzler, didn't produce anything either, then he, and everyone else, was going to be in deep trouble. The beer would run out, for one thing.

The reason why we're all big beer drinkers is we've got to save the water to keep the blasted geraniums alive . . .
—ROBERT B. GOODMAN and GEORGE JOHNSTON: *The Australians*, Rigby, Ltd., Adelaide, 1966

International finance, dollar devaluation, balance of payments, all were esoteric concepts in which the man in the pub had little interest. They were too remote, too complex, too badly explained in the available media for him to be interested. Most of the papers he read, or the radio stations he listened to, brought him the latest results of the horse races, the dog races, the cricket and soccer and football matches, and that was enough. The serious newspapers were read mostly by the intellectuals and financiers, and they had prepared them, anyway. So wot's in it for 'im?

Still, there remained other avenues to explore. Incentive pay (as in the mines) was one way. A person was paid for what he could produce, if it was of a quality that was marketable. Productivity was thus rewarded. It wasn't the number of hours one put in, but how well one performed. Some people liked the discipline of long hours. Some didn't. Why not let them make their own choice and pay them for what they did?

Well, it might be worth trying on an experimental basis. Nothing to lose, perhaps much to gain: not only for Australia, but for the rest of the technological world.

Experiments in corporate and industrial democracy also could be tried. Why is it that workingmen can vote for the prime minister or president of their country, but cannot vote for the chairman of the board or the president of the corporation for which they work? Might be interesting to find out. Where better than in Australia?

The trade union movement in Australia might not necessarily follow the American or English patterns. The difference between the American movement and that of the Australians, is that the Americans concentrated their power on securing higher economic benefits, while the Australian movement was largely based on aversion to any kind of authority. This was the non-economic, highly ethical implementation of the sea-dog, convict, Bushman syndrome.

The question was, would the organized workmen ever support any sort of reform program or change system that was dictated by the elite? Circumstances, such as a changing world trade pattern might force them to do so. But it seemed unlikely in the next three decades.

> **Australia has been pictured so often as a fair and youthful princess that it is forgotten that she was born and bred as an ill-favoured by-blow of the squalor and criminality of eighteenth century industrial England and the poverty of Ireland. For her first decades she was little more than a dirty Cinderella, smudged with ashes and cinders. Would it be surprising if a few of her early slatternly habits have survived?**
> —T. INGLIS MOORE: *Social Patterns in Australian Literature,* Angus and Robertson, Pty. Ltd. Sydney, 1971

The struggle for freedom on the part of the Australians was a linear ascent from the English Magna Carta and the American Bill of Rights. That it was not old enough to embrace the United Nations "Bill of Human Rights," was a measure of its immaturity, but this did not preclude the possibility that it might do so—in its own Australian way and in its own Australian time.

Like his English/European forebearers, the white Australian has a fierce pride in his country. This has been most usually expressed in a military form of nationalism. The Anzacs of Gallipoli and the Rats of Tobruk are good examples. Monuments to them dot the inhabited areas.

But sometimes pride expressed itself in terms of the size, climate and topography of the land itself.

> **The territory this nation occupies is of sufficient extent to admit of practically indefinite expansion in numbers, and is so situated that whoever occupies it must necessarily be dominant in this quarter of the globe. In itself it has the promise of greatness, and its surroundings are eminently favourable. Sufficiently isolated to run little risk of being involved in the strifes of the nations that are nearest, it is not too far distant for peaceful intercourse and the purposes of trade.**
> —H. T. BURGESS: *Year Book of Australia,* 1888

> **We have a climate incomparably superior to Great Britain; we have widespread material prosperity; we have absolutely no undeserved pauperism; and we have organizations and institutions for the promotion of scientific, artistic, educational, moral and philanthropical objects, which, in proportion to population, are unsurpassed in the world.**
> —HENRY GYLES TURNER: "Advance Australia," *Melbourne Review,* April, 1882

It would be interesting to see if this pride could be translated by the Australians into making their country a model for the world. Nearly every other country had largely destroyed its natural beauty in the interests of growth and development.

It is true that few Australians found beauty in their land and quite a few found it downright ugly. To the extent that it differed from the countryside of England with its nicely cropped lawns and clipped hedges—to that extent it was "wilderness." Their idea of "order" was control.

Helping Aborigines where it matters

Storefront law and medicine have come to Australia

Shirley Smith is a little too earthy, a little too substantial to be aptly called either the guardian or avenging angel of the Aboriginal community but her work with the Aboriginal Medical Service in Sydney gives her the opportunity to be both.

She cajoles, berates and browbeats her own people to use the service, and heed to the advice of the white doctors who work for it. She provides the vital and necessary link between the Aborigines and the professional men, just as Gordon Briscoe, field officer for the Aboriginal Legal Service, is the liaison between Aborigines in trouble with the law and the lawyers who work for the service.

Though both services were only begun in Sydney last year they are already well established and are being studied by groups in other States interested in setting up similar services.

keep them off the streets and out of sight because they offend the sensibilities of the more affluent.

Law as 'a white institution'

"In the case of the Aboriginal, the problem is aggravated by the historical relationship. When the white people occupied Australia they deprived the Aborigines of all rights, and used the law to legitimise this deprivation. So Aborigines tend to see law as the white institution.

The Aboriginal Legal Service is showing Aborigines how to regain their rights, and how to use the law, not only in criminal proceedings but for all types of legal problems, including tenancy, housing, hire-purchase.

IS THE DOOR CLOSING ON THE AGE OF DISCOVERY?

Very few of them knew how to do any of those things when they started out. But they learned, or they perished. Each man who survives must have learned to do everything for himself, to cope with every sort of emergency, to battle through every sort of difficulty — alone. So they are bound to become *self-contained, self-sufficient, self-reliant, extraordinarily independent and resourceful* . . . as no townspeople, and no village people, anywhere in the world, ever could be.

A. E. MANDER, *The Making of the Australians* (Melbourne 1958) pp. 25, 26.

Painting by
PRO HART

The sheep kept the grass cropped to the "right" height so that much of Australia, and of Australasia generally, looked like the fairways of a golf course. The native trees were cut down to increase the pasturage and were burned in giant wind-rows. One result was the destruction of what had been a naturally functioning ecosystem. In some places, there was substituted a pattern of erosion and floods, and eventually the abandonment of a ravaged land. Would this pattern continue? One did not know. What one did know was that all those ringed trees, which were going to die to make room for more sheep, were not going to help the Australians nor their neighbors very much.

There also was another kind of pride. It was pride in a sea-faring background; a rough, tough person who built an empire in far places with his skill and his courage.

He was an Anglo-Australian in the process of being hammered out of existence by a climate in which the true British type cannot subsist. The Englishman qua Englishman does not know how to permanently thrive far from the sea. It is the absolute negation of his whole nature. He is the child of the sailors of the French wars, the grandchild of the Elizabethan "sea-dogs," and the great-grandchild of the Jutland "sea-wolves"; and if he is to become the inhabitant of an earthbound interior, where no sea-breeze ever penetrates, he must renounce his essential being.
— FRANCIS ADAMS: *The Labour Movement in Australia,* (1891), Sun Books, Melbourne, 1968

The "sea-dog" was the vision of a hard, young man who took his flogging without a whimper; who faced the growling, roaring sea with the kind of courage it takes on the battlefield. Everyone who came to Australia (before aircraft) came by ship, most of them from England; the longest sea voyage in the world. Those who survived the ordeal had been winnowed out by time and two great oceans. Rather naturally, those who survived took pride in the fact that they did. It was a physical survival, based on brute strength, or heredity, or whatever. When the writers began to describe them, this trait was amplified.

The Bushman was the land version of the legendary sea-dog He, too, was resilient, tough and resourceful. He sailed upon the land as his predecessors had upon the sea. The two images reinforced themselves.

A little heat more or less, a little extra wayfaring, the prevalence of the orange and banana, of abundant food — these things do not suffice to relax the fibre and lower the stamina of the bold sea-roving breed which has never counted the cost of the deadliest climate or the wildest sea where honour was to be satisfied, thirst for adventure to be slaked, or even that lower but essential desideratum, a full purse to be secured. If the air be hot, there sighs the ocean breeze to temper it withal. On the great interior plateaus, the pure, dry atmosphere, which invigorates the invalid, rears up uninjured the hardy broods of the farmer, the stockrider, and the shepherd. Stalwart men and whole-some, stirring lasses do they make.

When will people cease to talk of "Australians" doing this and that, or permit colonists to differ among themselves from birth, as elsewhere? Here, under the Southern Cross, as under Ursa Major, are born the imaginative and the practical, the energetic, the dreamy, the slow and the brilliant, the cautious and the rash, the persevering and the fickle. As the inscrutable human unit enters the world, so must he or she remain, I hold, but partially modified by human agency, until the day of death. Change of abode or circumstance will not perceptibly alter the mysteriously-persistent entity.
— ROLF BOLDREWOOD: "The Australian Native-Born Type," *In Bad Company,* 1901

What came out of it was a self-view that was just as mythic as its sea-faring proto-type. It was a sort of fantasy — as in the

"The Secret Life of Walter Mitty"—and it didn't do any harm. Perhaps, to cope with this strange land, it might even have helped. But in retrospect, it was a fantasy, just the same.

The Bushman had as his earlier counterpart the legend of the American cowboy. He was a sort of a "High Noon" character, walking down that deserted street alone to shoot it out with the "bad" guys. Actually, the American cowboy lived a hard, cruel, dirty life. If he found himself at times on Main Street, he would head for the closest bar.

And so it was with the land-cruising sailor—the Bushman. "Where's the nearest pub, mate?"

It seemed that both the cowboy and the Bushman contributed to a certain shared self-image for the 20th Century man to emulate; tough, resilient, resourceful. A man for all seasons. It was not a bad image to have, even if one had never been out of a grubby little office on Collins Street in Melbourne for most of his adult life. It was something to identify with and to cling to. And perhaps, on holiday, to live up to. In a bureaucratic society, there wasn't much more for a man, who thought of himself in that way, to do.

> With steps that were limping and slow,
> With feet that were weary and sore,
> A sundowner tramped with a sundowner's swag
> On his back and a billy before—
>   Tramp, tramp, tramp,
> From the dawn till the shadows of night
> Creep out from the trees, like a thief from his camp,
> And never a station in sight.

—JOHN PHILIP BURKE, "His Last Stage," from *The Pacific Book of Bush Ballads*, Angus & Robertson Ltd., Sydney, 1967.

There were other inputs as well; among them, that of the convict colonist. This semi-legendary figure had a trait in common with the later Bushman: he hated authority and when he had the guts and stamina to do it, the convict disappeared into the bush, and if he survived, was transformed into a Bushman. The metamorphosis took place because of the hard pressures of the environment in which the escaped convict found himself. But at least he got there because he wanted to, and not because someone told him to.

All of this seemed long ago and irrelevant to what the Australian might do in the year 2000.

But it wasn't really irrelevant. By putting these inputs (sea-dog, convict, Bushman, landed aristocracy, the settlers) together one might get a pretty good idea of how the Australians were reacting now, and how they might react a generation hence.

First, to find how they might react, one pushed the "now" button.

"Now" was, of course, a state of mind. A hundred years—or a couple of hundred— would only be a heart beat in the time of man. But, for the white Australians, so shortly on the continent, it had seemed a long time.

How would the Australians be likely to react to increased bureaucracy and federal and state intervention in their lives?

One answer had been given earlier, and it did not seem that it would be likely to change much in the next thirty years.

41

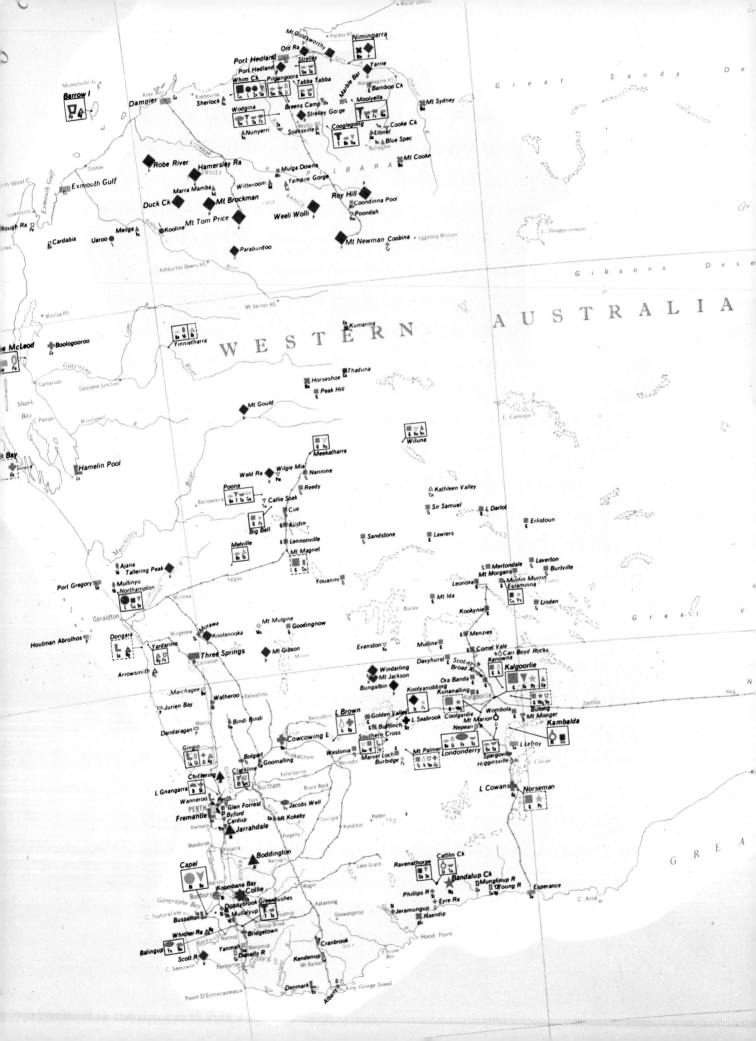

Standing there now in the enormous room that formed the center of his laboratory, he felt a slight undulation under his widespread feet, as if the whole place were floating upon some tranquil, timeless sea. He checked his bearings and found that he was, indeed, afloat and under way. He could but dimly remember the port of his departure, nor was he quite sure what his destination might be.

On the quarterdeck of this floating continent, one might feel somewhat like the captain of a ship in wartime, waiting until the vessel cleared the harbor before opening the sealed orders in the purser's safe to find out where one was supposed to be going to now.

This stone raft had been voyaging for such a long time and there had been so many ports of call, one could scarcely be expected to remember them all. Still one could look back into the ship's log and discover where it had been on the last trip. The entries in the log were blurred by the rains of time, but it did seem that the latest trip had started about 100 million years or so ago.

While parts of the world were still shifting, writhing and changing, throwing up Himalayas and Alps and Atlases and Cordilleras, Australia's extensive Pre-Cambrian area had already settled into its future shape. The continent had been formed and it was empty and already it was beginning to wear away under the rain, the wind, and the dust. When man finally did come to this continent, on the most belated of his journeyings across the planet, he was faced by an awesome intimidation . . . The shock of this confrontation has to this day left his mark upon him . . . All that is Australia begins not with man but with the land itself; and all the dramas of today's Australia are played in the eternal presence of Ancient beginnings, which is the land . . .
—ROBERT R. GOODMAN & GEORGE JOHNSTON: *The Australians*, Rigby, Ltd., Adelaide, 1966

This land lay down to sleep while the rest of the continents were still tossing and turning. Out of this, one might derive the aboriginal concept of "Dreamtime," with all its ramifications in the subconscious of the Australian mind. The continent was taking a nap in the afternoon of the world.

It was a light tap on the shoulder by a stranger from outer space that began—

quite slowly—to awaken it.

Between the time-blurred entries in the raft's log, it was dimly possible to make something out of its earlier peregrinations. The entries in the stone raft's log were a little hard to read. Mostly they were computer read-outs of measurements from deep-hole borings, changes in magnetic fields (the world's compass aswing), temperature gradients, earth plate tectonics, and some little hieroglyphic notes about the behavior of rectangular plates on the curvature of a small, diffident planet. Far as one could make out, the stone raft was riding on one of the plates which, itself, was an even larger stone raft riding on a sea of molten rock.

It seems unlikely that all the continents were collected in a single block for 4,000 million years and then broke apart and started their wanderings during the past 100 million years. It is more likely that the processes we see today have always been in action and that all through geologic time there have been moving plates carrying continents which have split many times and formed new oceans and sometimes to have collided and been welded together.
—SIR EDWARD BULLARD: "The Origin of the Oceans," *Scientific American*, Sept., 1969

One might assume that the raft had begun floating four-and-a-half billion years ago, but the log did not go back that far. Anyway, it had, over the millenia, changed names. The earliest entry in the raft's log was "Pangaea." One checked the available navigational charts, couldn't find anyplace called "Pangaea."

There were a few mildewed books in the chart room and since the pilot hadn't cleared the bar yet, there was time to look up "Pangaea." It seemed to have been a super-continent ("Pangaea" means "all lands") that later broke up into two super-continents called "Laurasia" in the north, and "Gondwanaland" in the south.

So, once upon a place and once within a time, there seemed to have been this great land mass now called Gondwanaland. Like the "lost continents" of Mu and Atlantis, Gondwanaland may have been but a myth; a fantasy of "faery lands forlorn." One knew intuitively that there were many other worlds and that one had such forgetfulness that he remembered them. But only dimly.

In the coldly rational night of one's probing mind, there did appear to be acceptable evidence (rationally? logically? scientifically?) that there once was a single great land mass in the southern hemisphere. The Greek philosophers had said so more than 2,000 years ago; and they had proven seldom to be wrong.

Captain Cook, no philosopher, but a first rate seaman, confirmed it empirically. And, for his efforts, was eaten by cannibals on some forgotten South Seas barricade. But you can't win them all.

Back to a place or a myth (they're both the same) called Gondwanaland. Say that because of the spin and wobble of the globe (blame the Moon!), the shrinking of the planet's crust (blame the Sun!) and perhaps because of gravitational changes yet unexplained (blame Einstein!), Gondwanaland fractured and broke up.

Its fragments drifted away like wayward teenagers in the dawn of the world. India and Australia grew up to be rather ordinary middle class citizens in the geological society; their forest-hair cut short, a little fat about the middle, somewhat slow to move, and looking forward to retirement and a relatively pleasant old age. True, they were a little bothered by earthquakes, and a volcano erupting now and then. But that was to be expected from the geologic young; they were always doing demonstrations and attracting attention to themselves by disrupting the order of things.

One of Gondwanaland's children, Australia, at this moment in geological time, appeared to be in a holding pattern, creeping northward at a rate of about three inches a year. It might bump into New Guinea and shove it aside like a defensive football lineman, or simply push New Guinea ahead of it, like some enormous bulldozer would shove a great new boulder.

Antarctica remained, held its position, balancing the land and ice mass of the other pole on the spinning, wobbling globe that some people called Earth.

The good stone raft now called Australia appeared to have cast off its lines and set off on its voyage, leaving behind its mother raft, now called Antarctica, many millions of years ago.

Navigational aids were not too sophisticated during that period and somehow, in the straits of time, the vessels became separated, each riding its own sea of molten stone on its crustal plate. There was another sister-ship—now called India— whose sails must have been better set, or something, because it raced faster north until it collided with Laurasia. The bump may have caused the Himalayas.

We can visualize the continents as being passively rafted over the surface of the globe as embedded plateaus of granite-like rock resting on the even larger and thicker crustal plates. The continents have generally maintained their size and shape since the breakup of Pangaea.
—ROBERT S. DIETZ and JOHN·C. HOLDEN: "The Breakup of Pangaea," *Scientific American*, Oct., 1970

And so through the double glass
windows, we watched the heat-hazy
plains drift by, stripped to their topsoil,
thinly clothed with saltbush and blue-
bush, with an absurd toy tree set here
and there like some shaggy toadstool on
the sand. The dusty, dry landscapes
passed by as if in a dream. Their harsh-
ness was muted by the cool air within.
At Rawlina, the guard told me, the outside temperature was 120 degrees.
'In the shade, you mean?' 'What shade?'

—GEORGE FARWELL, "Australian
Landscapes," Walkabout Pocketbook,
Sydney, 1969

We who look outward to the sun
And dream of things we might have done,
See visions of a spirit's flight
Beyond the sight, far lost in light.
Yet is no mountain top more fair
Than kindly hearth-smoke climbing on
    the air!

—MARY GILMORE, "Of Women,"
Selected Verse, Angus and Robertson,
Sydney, 1948

PRO HART

The history of Pangaea remains to be written. But the name is not particularly important; the dynamics are. Sir Edward Bullard suggests: "The picture is simple: the greatest part of the earth's surface is divided into plates . . . These plates move as rigid bodies, the new material for them being produced from the upper mantle by lava emerging from the crest of a mid-ocean ridge. Plates are destroyed at the oceanic trenches by plunging into the mantle, where ultimately they are mixed again with the material whence they came."

It didn't seem like a very safe ship to be on, but there weren't any others, and the time span of hundreds of millions of years gave one a little time to man the lifeboats.

Sir Edward's observations seemed to be backed up by Messrs. Dietz and Holden, or perhaps it was the other way around.

The guiding rationale . . . is the drift mechanism associated with plate tectonics and sea floor spreading . . . According to this concept the earth has a strong litho-sphere, or outer shell of rock, about 100 kilometers (62 miles) thick. Presumably, in response to forces generated in the astenosphere (the weak mantle of rock underlying the lithosphere) the shell was broken up into a number of separate plates. There are now some ten major plates, plus numerous additional sub-plates. The continents resting on these plates were rafted across the surface of the globe.
—ROBERT S. DIETZ and JOHN C. HOLDEN

Now, all of this might seem a little irrelevant to where the stone raft was headed by the year 2000, but if one does not know where one has been, how can one figure out where one was going? Again, the past may be no guide to the future, but if it's not, then what is?

Perhaps there was here something about the crew; and it was a rather motley crew in terms of all the other rafts floating around the world. Except if it really did break off from "Pangaea" in the very remote past, it was hard to account for the crew. Perhaps the duck-billed platypus swam there, and the kangaroo and wallaby hopped there, and the koala clung to a eucalyptus branch and floated the 10,000 miles there. It didn't seem likely, but then anything was possible in this strange land, and only the impossible could be believed. And sometimes, not even then. No one could have made up the hairy-nosed wombat; only the continent itself could have conjured up that image.

Well, you could go on this billion-year trip forever and never get anywhere by riding this stone raft on something called the Pacific—which was anything but pacific.

The cyclones roared down the "bowling alley" between the mainland and The Reef. Sometimes they flattened out whole communities: Magnetic Island or Chapman. Or, on the mainland, Cooktown and Cairns.

On the other coast, the hurricanes could wipe out whole communities from Perth to Darwin, an arc of unpredictable violence 1,800 miles long. There was Geraldton (red-brick houses, long air-strip); Carnarvon (much the same); Exmouth (a mosaic of red and green estuarian lagoons); Barrow Isle (the airfield facilities two empty gas drums, sun and flies—three trees on the other side of the island); Dampier (a long dock, high tides and manta rays nearly as big as the ore-ships; both gulping—one plankton, the other iron ore for Japan); Port Hedland (the beach so littered with exotic shells one could hardly count them); Broome and then Darwin. This was the hurricane coast; Darwin had been wiped out many times since the white man got there.

Along this arc, the Indian Ocean did its thing; winds up to 180 miles per hour, waves at 60 feet, enough to sink an ocean-going vessel.

The hurricane coast was part of this land —1,800 miles of coastland of it. The white western European somehow survived there. He dredged the harbour entrances, built little air-conditioned houses, desalinization plants for fresh water, pubs and recreation centers, window-screened against the flies; put underwater steel-wire fences in his ocean swimming pools to keep out the sharks and, in a part of the country where before only the rock wallaby could live, built libraries and even theatres. It was no mean accomplishment.

It was, however, a game the white man could never win using Old World techniques. But he had made a good first move and perhaps in a hundred years or so, the black and brooding continent might make *its* move. It was, at best, a dangerous game; at worst a disastrous one. But whatever happened, it was at least exciting and challenging. Because he was a born gambler he would play it out—whatever the odds.

The coasts were important to him, because that was where most of the people were. But the interior was by far the largest part of this enormous room. Not many people there—all together they would hardly make up enough to fill River City, Iowa, U.S.A.—but perhaps they were the most important people of all.

There, in the center of the room was a town called Alice. And a river called The Todd. Because there was so little water there, the annual regatta was run in the dry river bed with the men carrying their canoes on their heads. There was also an

Alice Springs Surfing Club, with T-shirts to match. The closest surf was 1,800 miles away, in any direction.

He chuckled a little, and went on his morning rounds.

He found he had strolled north to Papua/New Guinea, one of the largest islands on the globe. Here there were beautiful rain forests, cascading waterfalls that fell forever, rivers that flowed all year 'round. In the central highlands, there were stands of virgin hardwood—hard as iron, black as ebony, scarcely touched. Through the forest stands and in the paddocks, roamed the Black Angus and Brahman cattle. They ate the undergrowth and thus reduced the possibility of forest fires. They were sleek and even resisted the fierce ticks of this tropical country. They would end up eventually as premium beef, flown to Lae and then to Japan. They walked in the paddocks like promises to be fulfilled.

Most of the people, too, were black. No one seems to know where they came from originally, but they were there. Perhaps blood tests run on computers on the indigenous races of Melanesia and Polynesia would establish from whence these people came. Anyway, it probably didn't matter, except to anthropologists. The aborigines were a hardy, ingenious race not related to the Australian aborigine. They had already, after 200 years of colonial rule, achieved independence; had elected their own Parliament, and even might come up with some new political styles that would shake the world, in the next 30 years.

Papua/New Guinea (He called it PING for short) was the giant steppingstone to

OIL!
A bright picture now, but don't forget the past

the markets and cultures of Asia. It would be a long walk, but it was the road he'd have to take; no other alternatives seemed to be open.

Well, it was pretty hot here and he thought he might as well go to the fridge—Antarctica—and see if there was beer there, in the vast emptiness of the world's last virtually uninhabited continent.

It was a larger continent than Australia and perhaps even richer in minerals, which, given the galloping technology of his time, might be developed within the 30-year time span he was considering. Might be, he wasn't sure.

As he took his beer from the fridge, he wondered what, if anything could be done with it. Not the beer, being Australian he knew what to do with that, but what about the fridge? It was a big one, covering some 5 and 3/4 million square miles (13½ million square kilometers). One problem was that there was a lot of ice in the fridge; probably needed defrosting.

Suppose the fridge in Antarctica was partially defrosted? Some of the congealed ice could be floated to Australia and used as sources of fresh water in coastal areas.

Two scientists have estimated that if an iceberg 250 yards thick and 2,700 yards across were towed to Australia, it would provide 207 billion gallons of water—even though 70 percent of the iceberg would melt during the trip. They estimate that a seagoing tug could make the voyage for less than $1,000,000; that the fresh water obtained from the iceberg would be worth about $5,500,000, or less than a tenth of the cost of an equivalent amount of desalted sea water.

—World Almanac, 1971, *Saturday Review*, October 23, 1971, Pg. 20

Interesting as this proposition might be, there are some serious practical problems. Where would one anchor an iceberg? There are not many deep water anchorages in Australia. Those that are there are already filled with ships. Do you displace the ships to make room for the iceberg? Or build new deep anchorages? Either way would be very expensive. Even assuming that iceberg anchorages could be built, how would the water be pumped far enough inland to do any good? One would need some source of power. Petroleum? 30 percent imported. Coal? No, it's exported. Atomic energy? First place, don't have it; second place, if one had it, it could desalt sea water cheaper than towing icebergs with no parking space when you got there.

Icebergs from Antarctica did not seem a very good solution, at least within the thirty year time span. So what else is new?

With two oceans (the Pacific and the Indian) to draw from, plus the Antarctic Southern Ocean, there seemed a good possibility to get fresh water along the coastal areas through a system of desalting plants. Assuming there was sufficient energy, the fresh water could be pumped inland a couple of hundred miles or so. (About 124.27 kilometers.)

Here, again, the problem was what the source of energy might be. Atomic seemed the only answer. But who would pay for the nuclear plants? They would be very expensive to build and it seemed doubtful that farmers in the interior would have enough money to pay for either the water or the electricity at rates high enough to make the plans profitable unless they were highly subsidized by the Commonwealth government or the states; none of which had any money anyway.

In the long term, nuclear generating stations may perhaps supplant all other types for base load generation. Up to the present, however, Australia has not yet adopted nuclear generation. The relative costs of electricity produced by conventional and nuclear generating stations depend on many factors, the two most critical being the capital cost for nuclear plant and the cost of fuel for conventional thermal plant. Nuclear plant, to a degree greater than any other type of plant, has a decreasing cost per kilowatt installed as the unit size increases.
In Australia, the systems large enough to accept nuclear plants of reasonably economic size are in the states which have very cheap coal. By contrast, the states with more expensive and inadequate deposits have smaller electrical systems and could only consider generating units in sizes for which the unit capital cost of nuclear plants would be high.
However, the gap between costs based on nuclear and fossil fuels is steadily narrowing.
— "Electricity," Electricity, Water, Power and Geographic Branch, Department of National Development, Canberra, 1969.

If the atomic nations—U. S. A., Russia, France or China wanted to set up experimental nuclear plants, and were willing to pay for them, then perhaps an offshoot might be desalted water and the electrical power to pump it inland. This was a long shot that might race home first in thirty years, but with galloping technology, might not finish at all. Not a very good bet, even for people who would bet on anything that had a chance; cockroaches racing down a table for a breadcrumb, tarantulas jumping for a fly, dingoes racing for a rabbit, cricket and soccer and football. No bet, mate.

Careful studies of the trend in the cost of nuclear power stations and the power produced in them, point to the fact that in the middle Seventies, in Australia, 500 megawatt nuclear power stations will compete with New South Wales coal. This position will improve as time goes by and Australia may expect to see a major programme in the construction of nuclear power stations in N.S.W., Victoria and probably South and Western Australia from the middle Seventies through to the late Eighties.
— National Development Quarterly, March, 1970.

The major problem was that the atomic plants would be working against a self-defeating gradient, since the coastal mountains sloped down to the sea. Downhill all the way. At some point in the energy transaction there would be a point of no return. No return on the investment, anyway.

It was a puzzlement (to draw on a phrase from "The King and I") but not an insurmountable one. It could be that there were locations that could be found and developed where there were sufficient markets for atomically produced fresh water, electric power, mineral byproducts from the desalting process and the sale of radioisotopes.

But there were other ways the problem of getting water inland could be approached.

For more than a decade past . . . atomic energy has been playing a part in Australian life. Great progress is being made in the application of nuclear materials in the fight against disease and in the manufacture of many commonplace products . . . Even though major developments in atomic energy lie before us, it has already become an indispensable part of daily life in Australia.
—"Many Applications for Atomic Energy," *National Development Quarterly*, June, 1971.

One could try an interlocking system of natural power systems that would do no environmental damage, use up no resources, but would simply channel

Japanese and French plan to build $200m uranium plant

Dr Strangelove's nuclear oversell

The prospects of using peaceful nuclear explosions are often painted in alluring tones, but the uncertainties and unknowns are rarely discussed. It is time to appraise realities behind the salesmanship.

Nuclear giants want deal with Australia

Australia plays a key role in the Pacific nuclear race

existing power sources to desalinate the water and provide power to pump it far enough inland to do some good. This would please the environmentalists, and the farmers and almost everyone except the oil, gas and coal interests; but their time was so limited it didn't matter anyway.

How would one go about setting up such a "natural" system? One could start at those places on the coast that had high tides or high surf, or both. Floating oil drums, or something like them, connected by universal transmission systems (let's call them "Surfriders") through contemporary electronic devices, convert the rise and fall of the tides and the rotary motion of the waves into electrical current that could be sent to shore by cable. The drums, or whatever, could be anchored to sunken, abandoned automobiles (plus some concrete slabs) which would form a reef for the protection of small sea life, and ultimately provide a source of food.

The shore-based plant could consist of an interlocking system of power systems with a provision for energy storage and transmission. Other energy collectors, could include:

An array of solar power collectors, much like those on the space satellites, to transform solar rays into electrical current. Given the high solar ray intensity in Australia this system should be productive, in most areas, most of the year. The solar collector plates could form the roof of the acres-wide building that would house the desalinization plant and provide energy to supplement the tidal and wave energy input.

On the perimeter of the complex there could be windmills, because on the coastal

Waiting for a dividend from atoms

Many applications for atomic energy

NUCLEAR POWER
Stations set up 'by 1980 s'

areas where there are high tides and high surf configurations, there is also a lot of wind. The windmills could add to the input of the tidal and solar inputs, and in some places, could draw up fresh water. So there could be an exponential factor of three, in the right place and at the right times.

Once in awhile it rains like hell in these areas (the ones with the tidal and solar and wind power) and so it might be possible to design and build "rainmills" which operate vertically instead of horizontally, as the windmills do. The rainmills, during periods of intense rainfall (and sometimes it *is* intense) could feed still more power through generators, and could be supplemented further by rain catchment tanks that could store water that runs down during dry spells and turns generators. At least such a system would be a fourth potential energy input, and the fresh water would reduce the amount of desalinization required.

(It was, he mused, much like the American slaughterhouses that used "everything of the pig but its squeal." This unmarketable product ended up as the automobile horn. So, one never knows what treasures may be hidden in the technological underground.)

Once one puts them all together—the sea and the sun, the wind and the rain—and converts their energy into electrical power, there still remains a problem; what does one do with it?

Part of it would be used for the desalinization project. Part would be used to send the fresh water to communities and farms inland.

Perhaps a little of the power could be used for radio and TV stations, which might develop sources of revenue from the big cities.

Some of the electrical energy could be stored in mercury-cadmium batteries to keep things going when the tide didn't come in, the waves stopped running high, the sun was screened out by overcast, the wind had stopped and there was no rain in sight. Such storage batteries already existed; perhaps even better ones could be developed in the next thirty years.

So, one might have electrical power and desalted water, using up no mineral nor organic resources, and creating no air or water pollution of any kind.

There seemed to be some interesting by-products out of such an organic and systemic operation.

Minerals extracted from the salt water processing system might find a market. They would have been extracted from the sea water without bulldozers ripping up the land. These minerals and metals could include sodium, chlorine, magnesium and many, many others. It might be that there would be enough left over from the desalting and the pumping to rough-process, or beneficiate, the residue and thus make it profitably marketable.

Such a complex would need some sort of cooling system, and perhaps the warm water that had to be expended could be used for hydroponic gardens to raise vegetables (using part of the residual chemicals from the desalting process as nutrients) and part of the warm water could be used to raise tropical fish in ponds; the same breeder stock of fish that were given a chance to multiply on the man-made reef of abandoned automobiles which helped to anchor the oil-drum "surfriders" that began the whole system of systems in the first place.

According to seismic surveys, under the Australian continental mantle, there were, inland, vast reservoirs of "fossilized" water. This was water that was trapped beneath the stone raft of Australia. Some of it may have come from Antarctic icebergs on their northward migration. Most of it probably came there through the filtering of sea water through the reefs and the interstices of the stone raft itself. This could have happened a billion or two billion years ago. Anyway, the water is there; fresh and pure, and it's lying under the dry parts of the continent. It had ended up, like a joey in its mama kangaroo's pouch, in underground pockets of the stone raft.

These pockets are pretty far down, and hard to reach, but with contemporary oil drilling techniques they could be reached; providing anyone is willing to pay as much for water as for oil. But with the depletion of the world's known oil reserves, there might come a time within thirty years when water to grow vegetables and livestock would command the same price as petroleum. Could be at least worth thinking about. Other continents also had similar fossil water reservoirs, but no need to use them yet. Perhaps Australia could lead the way.

Once the fossil water was tapped, it would have to be pumped to the surface — some 12,000 feet of bore. This might be done through small nuclear powered pumps. Sky-crane helicopters could fly the

deep drilling equipment in and out. Smaller helicopters or even bush planes could supply the small amount of fuel necessary every three years or so. Once the system was going, water delivered at the surface should be relatively inexpensive. It was only that first cost that was important. Perhaps a consortium of other nations could provide the financing using Australian technological expertise.

It may have sounded like "The House That Jack Built." But each of the interacting systems had been used successfully in other countries. Why not try to put them all together? Tidal action, solar energy, wind power, rainfall and perhaps other forces we hardly have discovered yet.

There were some other considerations. One was the amount of salinity in the water that could be tolerated by existing species of plants and animals. These tolerances were based on European and American standards. There seemed to be no reason why, through biological engineering, there could not be developed plants and animals with a much higher salt tolerance, so that the desalinization job would not need to be so energy consuming. Many useful (to humans) species of plants thrive in saline waters. Some experiments in the Middle East have shown that native plants can be adapted to rather highly saline waters. "Salt water farming" appeared to be a definite possibility, using genetic engineering.

The development of species—plant or animal—that can tolerate high sodium/chlorine intakes may be the end part of the process that begin with those oil drums in the waves to form "some forgotten barricade" against man's ravaging of the planet.

It really did not seem to matter too much whether the scheme would work or not; at least it was an alternative solution to getting semi-fresh water inland on a paying basis.

It was, of course, only one of a number of possible alternatives that differed from the traditional, now dying, ways of the past.

Suppose the whole scheme wouldn't work out, it would cost too much money, it would yield too little, there still seemed to be many other ways to get semi-fresh water into the inland. Many other ways.

Thus in Central Australia, there seems to be water, water everywhere, but not a drop to drink. Just have to get down there and suck it up, like a giant straw. There would have to be some sort of state of Commonwealth regulation of the amount of output, so that the fossil water could be continuously replaced by the slow seepage and filtering process from the sea. Determining what that rate would be should not be beyond the ability of contemporary science.

All right, maybe there are too many drawbacks here. The small atomic pumps have not been designed yet. There is a paucity of big helicopters in Australia. Once done, deep bore drilling would

take a long time to pay off. But what's a long time? Ten—twenty—thirty years? Or even a hundred? Investment appreciates as productivity and marketing increases.

First, one has to have the water. Then raise the crops and livestock. Then build transport systems to markets. Again, one is considering interlocking systems, not isolated ones. It becomes fairly simple after that.

As one looked with a sort of detached amusement at what had been done and what could be done in the field of energy supply, one was struck by the paradox that, given a choice, humans almost always seemed to opt for the most expensive and ecologically destructive sources and processes. For instance, such technologically ridiculous sources as coal, petroleum, firewood, "natural" gas (ever heard of an "unnatural gas?") and uranium, thorium and tritium.

There were other sources close at hand, available to everyone, that could be processed economically into electrical or thermal energy for household and, in some cases, industrial use. One of these was wet garbage and sewage, or waste products from livestock and household pets.

When wet garbage and sewage decompose, bacterial action produces methane gas. This gas (the fuel of the "fox-fires" that dance above marshes at night) can be used as a source for heating, lighting, and even for powering automobiles—if indeed automobiles were still to exist by the year 2000.

A tank covered with a plastic bubble would trap the methane gas as it was generated by aneurobic bacteria and the gas could be stored for future use, just as other forms of natural gas are now. The plastic bubble would control odors and insect infestation. Since, in technological societies, the average family produces great quantities of wet waste every day, there should be enough methane gas generated to satisfy the normal needs of a family.

Such a home system would obviate sewage lines, septic tanks, light poles, and garbage collection and disposal. It could eliminate the urban problem of municipal garbage dumps and river, lake and ocean pollution from the pouring out of untreated sewage.

Publicly or commercially operated fossil-fuel or nuclear-powered generating plants could concentrate on serving the special needs of heavy industry, without having to build peak-capacity facilities to meet the requirements of family units. Transmission line rights-of-way acquisition, maintenance costs, and the voltage losses on long distance transmission could be greatly reduced. (Under the traditional systems, generating plants are most usually located a considerable distance from the metropolitan areas, their chief consuming market.)

If private homes, apartment buildings, and hotels could generate their own electrical and heating requirements from their occupants' wastes, the big generating plants could concentrate on industrial uses, most of which take place on the periphery of densely inhabited areas or in relatively compact "industrial parks" or commercially-zoned districts. With a limited number of contractual industrial clients, costs of billing, collecting, maintenance and meter reading could be greatly reduced.

What one could easily envisage was a combination system of solar energy collecting surfaces on buildings, and a methane producing system that could serve as a "standby" source of energy during periods of overcast when the solar collectors were operating at a minimum, and of course, during nights. Linked with storage batteries and an automatic temperature and voltage control system, a family could have as steady a source of electrical energy as now rendered by the traditional public utility generating plants—perhaps even more so—since industrial demand and occasional generating plant malfunction would not affect the continuous flow of power to "self-generating" residential areas.

Whether the Australians would undertake the development of such self-contained systems was problematic. As long as their attitude was caught up in the amber of 19th Century thinking, they would probably go on drilling for oil on the North Coast and Bass Straits and trying to get permission to do so on the Great Barrier Reef, continue to strip-mine coal on the Eastern parameter, and, in general, repeat the century-old errors of Europe and North America.

The subtle difference was that the Australians still had a choice to develop new energy systems.

Other countries and cultures did not have the option.

Certain areas of the Australian coastline have huge potential for tidal power development. It has been estimated, for example, that 300,000 megawatts of tidal power could be developed along the Kimberley coast of Western Australia. The sites, in common with others possessing large potential, are remote from major load centres, and the large expenditure needed for the necessary transmission lines cannot be justified at this stage.
—"Electricity," Water, Power and Geographic Branch, Department of National Development, Canberra, 1969.

Henry Lawson was perhaps the best
Australian writer of the 19th Century.
The "best" because he wrote honestly,
with neither pretense nor affectation.
The excerpt that appears below is
representative of some of his best
work. It says a lot about the
Australian's willingness to innovate,
and his sense of cosmic laughter.
At himself.
—HENRY LAWSON, "Joe Wilson's
Mates" Published by Lloyd O'Neil Pty.
Ltd., Hawthorn, Victoria, 1970

Dave Regan, Jim Bently, and
Andy Page were sinking a shaft
at Stony Creek in search of a
rich gold quartz reef which was
supposed to exist in the vicinity.
There is always a rich reef supposed to exist in the vicinity; the
only questions are whether it is
ten feet or hundreds beneath the
surface, and in which direction.
They had struck some pretty solid
rock, also water which kept them
bailing. They used the old-
fashioned blasting powder and
time-fuse. They'd make a sausage
or cartridge of blasting-powder
in a skin of strong calico or canvas,
the mouth sewn and bound round
the end of the fuse; they'd dip the
cartridge in melted tallow to make
it watertight, get the drill-hole as
dry as possible, drop in the cartridge with some dry dust, and
wad and ram with stiff clay and
broken brick. Then they'd light
the fuse and get out of the hole and
wait. The result was usually an
ugly pot-hole in the bottom of the
shaft and half a barrow-load of
broken rock.

There was plenty of fish in the
creek, fresh-water bream, cod,
cat-fish, and tailers. The party were
fond of fish . . . However, the creek
was low, just a chain of muddy
waterholes, from the hole with a
few bucketfuls in it to the sizable
pool with an average depth of six
or seven feet, and they could get
fish by bailing out the smaller holes
or muddying up the water in the
larger ones till the fish rose to the
surface.

Dave got an idea.

"Why not blow the fish up in the
big waterhole with a cartridge?"
he said. "I'll try it."

He made a cartridge about three
times the size of those they used
in the rock. The inner skin was of
stout calico; Andy stuck the end
of a six-foot piece of fuse well
down in the powder and bound
the mouth of the bag firmly to it
with whipcord. The idea was to
sink the cartridge in the water with
the open end of the fuse attached
to a float on the surface, ready for
lighting.

Round the cartridge Andy, at
Dave's suggestion, bound a strip
of sail canvas—that they used for
making water-bags—to increase
the force of the explosion, and
round that he pasted layers of stiff
brown paper—on the plan of the
sort of fireworks we called "gun-
crackers."

He dipped the cartridge in
melted tallow, twisted a length of
fencing-wire round it as an after-
thought, dipped it in tallow again,
and stood it carefully against a tent-
peg, and wound the fuse loosely
round it.

They had a big black young
retriever dog—or rather an over-
grown pup, a big, foolish, four-
footed mate, who was always

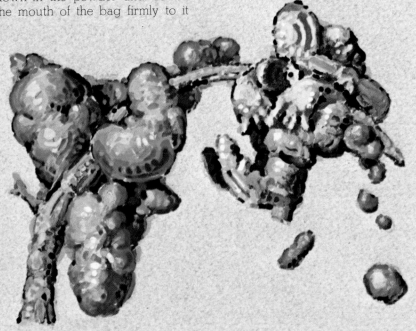

59

slobbering round them and lashing their legs with his heavy tail that swung round like a stock-whip. Most of his head was usually a red, idiotic slobbering grin of appreciation of his own silliness. He seemed to take life, the world, his two-legged mates, and his own instinct as a huge joke. He'd retrieve anything; he carted back most of the camp rubbish that Andy threw away.

He watched Andy with great interest all the morning making the cartridge, and hindered him considerably, trying to help. Andy was cook today; Dave and Jim stood with their backs to the fire, as bushmen do in all weathers, waiting till dinner should be ready.

Dave glanced over his shoulder to see how the chops were doing —and bolted. He explained afterwards that he thought he heard the pan spluttering extra, and looked to see if the chops were burning. Jim Bently looked behind and bolted after Dave. Andy stood stock-still, staring after them.

"Run, Andy! Run!" they shouted back at him. "Run! Look behind you, you fool!" Andy turned slowly and looked, and there, close behind him, was the retriever with the cartridge in his mouth—wedged into his broadest and silliest grin. And that wasn't all. The dog had come round the fire to Andy, and the loose end of the fuse had trailed and waggled over the burning sticks into the blaze; Andy had slit and nicked the firing end of the fuse well, and now it was hissing and spitting properly.

Andy's legs started with a jolt; his legs started before his brain did, and he made after Dave and Jim. And the dog followed Andy.

Dave and Jim were good runners—Jim the best—for a short

distance; Andy was slow and heavy, but he had the strength and the wind and could last. The dog capered round him, delighted as a dog could be to find his mates, as he thought, on for a frolic. Dave and Jim kept shouting back, "Don't foller us! Don't foller us, you coloured fool!" But Andy kept on, no matter how they dodged. The dog circled round Andy—the live fuse swishing in all directions and hissing and spluttering and stinking. Jim yelling to Dave not to follow him, Dave shouting to Andy to go in another direction—to "spread out," and Andy roaring at the dog to go home. Then Andy's brain began to work, stimulated by the crisis: he tried to get a running

kick at the dog, but the dog dodged; he snatched up sticks and stones and threw them at the dog and ran on again. The retriever saw that he'd made a mistake about Andy, and left him and bounded after Dave. Dave, who had the presence of mind to think that the fuse's time wasn't up yet, made a dive and a grab for the dog, caught him by the tail, and as he swung round snatched the cartridge out of his mouth and flung it as far as he could; the dog immediately bounded after it and retrieved it. Dave roared and cursed at the dog, who, seeing that Dave was offended, left him and went after Jim, who was well ahead. Jim swung to a sapling and went up it like a native bear; it was a young sapling, and Jim couldn't safely get more then ten or twelve feet from the ground. The dog laid the cartridge, as carefully as if it were a kitten, at the foot of the sapling, and capered and leaped and whooped joyously round under Jim. Jim tried to climb higher and the sapling bent and cracked. Jim fell on his feet and ran. The dog swooped on the cartridge and followed. It all took but a very few moments. Jim ran to a digger's hole, about ten feet deep, and dropped down into it—landing on soft mud—and was safe. The dog grinned sardonically down on him, over the edge, for a moment, as

if he thought it would be a good lark to drop the cartridge down on Jim.

"Go away, Tommy," said Jim feebly, "go away."

The dog bounded off after Dave, who was the only one in sight now; Andy had dropped behind a log, where he lay flat on his face.

There was a small hotel or shanty on the creek, on the main road, not far from the claim. Dave was desperate, the time flew much faster in his stimulated imagination than it did in reality, so he made for the shanty. There were several casual bushmen on the veranda and in the bar; Dave rushed into the bar, banging the door to behind him. "My dog!" he gasped, in reply to the astonished stare of the publican, "the blanky retriever—he's got a live cartridge in his mouth—"

The retriever, finding the front door shut against him, had bounded round and in by the back way, and now stood smiling in the doorway leading from the passage, the cartridge still in his mouth and the fuse spluttering. They burst out of that bar. Tommy bounded first after one and then after another, for, being a young dog, he tried to make friends with everybody.

The bushmen ran round cor-

ners, and some shut themselves in the stable.

The retriever went in under the kitchen, amongst the piles, but luckily for those inside, there was a vicious yellow mongrel cattle-dog sulking and nursing his nastiness under there. Tommy saw his danger—he'd had experience from this dog—and started out and across the yard, sticking to the cartridge. Halfway across the yard the yellow dog caught him and nipped him. Tommy dropped the cartridge, gave one terrified yell, and took to the bush. The yellow dog sniffed at the cart-

ridge twice, and was just taking a third cautious sniff when—

It was very good blasting-powder—a brand that Dave had recently got up from Sydney; and the cartridge had been excellently well made.

Bushmen say that that kitchen jumped off its piles and on again. When the smoke and dust cleared away, the remains of the nasty yellow dog were lying against the paling fence.

Dave decided to apologize later on, "when things had settled a bit," and went back to camp. And the dog that had done it all, Tommy, the great, idiotic mongrel retriever, came slobbering round Dave and lashing his legs with his tail, and trotted home after him, smiling his broadest, longest, and reddest smile of amiability, and apparently satisfied for one afternoon with the fun he'd had.

Andy chained the dog up securely, and cooked some more chops, while Dave went to help Jim out of the hole.

And most of this is why, for years afterwards, lanky, easy-going bushmen, riding lazily past Dave's camp, would cry, in a lazy drawl and with just a hint of the nasal twang:

"'Ello, Da-a-ve! How's the fishin' getting on, Da-a-ve?"

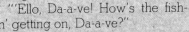

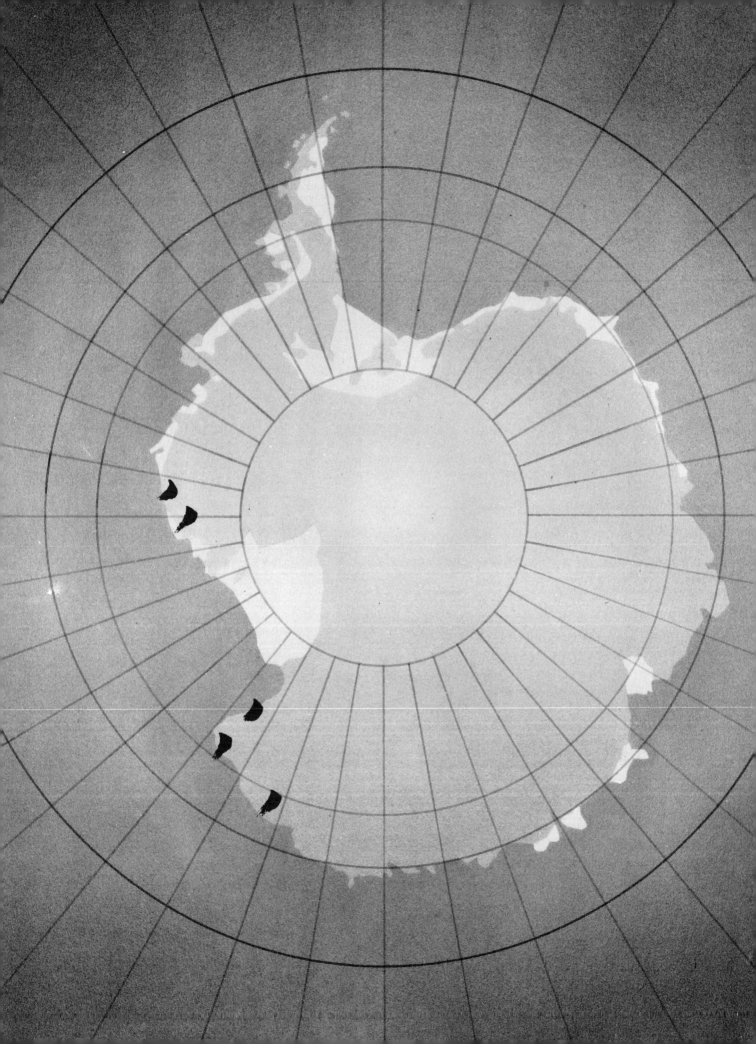

The port of departure for this strange Odyssey of The Stone Raft through space and time was locked in a frozen glare. It stared down the eons in an icy Cyclopean way, assuming without hope the day of no return. Beneath the neon silence of the voice of the solar wind, the great crystal cliffs split and tumbled, the detritus turned into white flocks of ice/sheep headed northward to their most certain doom. They were Antarctica's voice.

The frozen Atlas held its position, not shrugging, balancing the land and ice weight of the other pole on this spinning and wobbling globe. There had been a time, and now there appeared to be ample evidence of it, when Antarctica was a tropical or semi-tropical continent. The evidence was on the record; deep drilled ice cores, pollen counts, and most of all from the fossil remains of LYSTROSAURUS, a little fresh water reptile that had been found on the two roaming continents of India and Australia as well. Even with an outboard motor, this little creature could not have crossed the thousands of miles of surging salt water that separated the continents today.

So, relatives of this little creature must have ridden the stone rafts of his present tombland. All, except for the poor little waif of evolution who somehow got stranded in Antarctica and was buried in snows he did not know and under ice he could not imagine in his small reptilian mind. He would have no way of knowing that he would someday be famous. And he probably would not have cared. Given world enough and time . . .

One would leave him there, crouched in his multimillion year dream, and consider that Antarctica appeared to have been the mother continent for two other continents, India and Australia. They drifted away like wayward teenagers in the dawn of the world and grew up to be rather ordinary middle class citizens in the geological society; a little fat about the middle, a little slow to move and looking forward to re-tirement and a relatively pleasant old age.

Meanwhile, Mama Antarctica had problems at home. The house had gotten awfully cold after the children left. Nearly all of the rooms were coated with ice. Most of the year, one could not even get out the front door with all those ice packs lurking out there. She would have to wait for the April of her Spring, after the winter of her world.

But there were consolations. The old home had some attractions for the young at heart and so little by little they came "home" again, after an absence of millions and millions of years.

They came back because they were young and curious. They came back because it is only the unknown that is a magnet for the human mind. They came back because the only experience is a new experience.

For one thing, on a crowded earth, there was an awful lot of unpopulated space; some 5,300,000 square miles of it. One

---

Approximately 98 percent of Antarctica is covered by ice. The ice sheet contains about 90 percent of the world's fresh water , about 6 million cubic miles (34 million cubic kilometres), enough to raise the level of the world's oceans by about 200 feet (60 metres) if it should all melt. The mean thickness of the ice exceeds 6,000 feet (1,800 metres). The ice reaches a thickness of about 15,800 feet (4,800 metres) 350 miles (510 kilometres) south of Casey in Greater Antarctica. In Lesser Antarctica, the ice thickness exceeds 14,000 feet (4,250 metres) at a point about 100 miles (160 kilometres) east of Byrd Station. The ice under the South Pole is 9,219 feet (2,800 metres) thick and extends 33 feet (10 metres) below sea level. Much of the rock hidden by the ice is below sea level, some being as much as 8,300 feet (2,500 metres) below. If the ice were removed, the rock beneath would rise slowly by about a third of the former thickness of the ice.
—"Australians in the Antarctic," Pg. 3.

couldn't say that of any other continent. The air, the waters, the ground surface were almost unpolluted by man. True, there was some litter around the stations at McMurdo Sound, much like the debris that the astronauts had left on the moon. True, there was some contamination from DDT in the only living natives—the penguins and the Weddell seal. There was some poison from atomic fallout on the surface ice. But, all in all, it was the largest land area on the planet that man had not managed to damage irreparably.

Possibly most people wouldn't think of it that way, but this continent was a desert— a sort of frozen Sahara, only ten times as big.

Antarctica, a cold desert, receives little precipitation and this is in the form of snow. Over much of the continent, the mean annual snow accumulation is the equivalent of five inches (12 centimetres) of water, while on the central highland of Greater Antarctica accumulation is only the equivalent of two inches (5 centimetres) of water; around the coast mean annual accumulation is equivalent to 8-20 inches (20-50 centimetres) with an unusually high maximum of 36 inches (90 centimetres) equivalent at the base of the Antarctic Peninsula.
— "Australians in the Antarctic," Pg. 4.

Why not use this Antarctic house as a laboratory?

To study what?

Well, for one thing, one might study viruses that afflict other living organisms adversely.

At the Australian National University, there had been built a quite expensive laboratory for the sterile study of viruses. But in Antarctica, there already existed the conditions for sterile laboratories at sub-freezing temperatures. Given jet transport technology and suitable landing strips, the logistics of moving materials and technicians from Invercargill in South New

Zealand, or from South Africa, or from the tip of South America should be much less expensive and perhaps more efficacious than building sterile laboratories in or near such highly contaminated areas as Sydney, Melbourne, or any other place on the Australian continent.

On Antarctica, genetic studies also could be implemented more successfully than any other place in the world. Frozen sperm banks, not only for humans but for all other "endangered species," could be stored there indefinitely, along, of course, with the requisite ova banks. If a species of plant or animal really was in danger of extinction, the genetic blueprints could be brought back from out of the cold and given a new lease on life in a more permissive environment or in a more friendly time.

While some nations were considering the possibilities of larger or more sophisticated laboratories for space medicine research, it seemed at least possible that many of the environmental situations in which space travelers found themselves could be studied much less expensively and more quickly in Antarctica. Except for "gravitational weightlessness," most of the biological problems of man in space could be duplicated in caverns hollowed from the ice. In addition to medical problems, tests of such items as space suits, electronic control and communication systems could be reasonably close to the expensive space simulation environments built in warmer climes. At the very least, the Antarctic laboratories could serve as places where the information from space laboratories could be rechecked.

There was a growing interest in the preservation of human and animal bodies after death, in the hope that medical science would ultimately be able to bring them back to life again and to cure whatever caused their deaths to begin with (or end with). Such burials in crypts carved from the ice, using laser or ultrasonic techniques for the excavation, might be more economical than similar "holding patterns" on the other, much warmer continents. Cryobiotics required lower temperatures than those prevailing on the Antarctic continent, but the temperature gradient might be more easily and economically attained and maintained over long periods of time if one started at the low temperatures already available in Antarctica.

Here the transient bodies could sleep for millenia in their crystal crypts, awaiting now the second coming of a science that would bring a sort of immortality.

Another use for the disposal of human-created wastes would be those produced by nuclear power generating stations; a problem that could be worldwide by the year 2000. These waste products, partic-ularly the "high level" radioactive ones, constituted only one percent by volume of all radioactive wastes but produced about 90 percent of the total radioactivity. Some

of these wastes would continue to emit radiation for 250,000 years. And there was no safe place, ecologically speaking, to store them.

Except for one.

An ingenious solution has been proposed by three American scientists (E. Z. Zeller, D. F. Saunders and E. E. Angiko) in an article entitled "Putting Radioactive Wastes on Ice; A Proposal for an International Radionuclide in Antarctica," in the "Bulletin of the Atomic Scientists," January, 1973.

Capsules or containers of highly radio-active waste materials would simply be dropped like bombs on the ice by aircraft. The heat generated by the waste products would slowly melt a shaft down through the ice cap to depths of as much as one or two kilometers (about a mile and a quarter down). The waste canisters could be dropped with parachutes to minimize impact damage, and they could be designed in such a way as to come to rest somewhere above the bedrock. Snow, melted water and the plastic flow of ice should permanently seal the shafts created by the slowly descending containers. They, too, could be sealed in crystal crypts, awaiting whatever resurrection atoms might have.

While at first this looked like a fairly trivial technological suggestion, on second inspection it had some enormous implica-tions for the future. For one thing, the speed at which nuclear power generating plants could be built (to replace oil and coal burning generating plants, which would not only add to atmospheric pollu-tion, but would run out of fuel in 30 years or so, anyway) was largely dependent on what could be done with the radioactive waste products.

Some 36 nations already were building or had plans for building nuclear power generating plants. But in densely populated countries, which needed the nuclear-generated power the most, there was no place to put the wastes; no safe hiding place. The problem was complicated by the fact that for profitable operation a nuclear plant had to be located near large "service areas," with high density populations. Otherwise, transmission costs would make the electricity too expensive to use. But if the generating plants were close to urban centers, there would be no place to dispose of the wastes safely.

Australia had a particular interest in this problem because it not only had a power program based on nuclear plants, but some 85 percent of its population was concentrated on a narrow shelf along its southeast coast. One could surmise that the radioactive wastes could be buried in the vast deserts of the Outback. But this would involve the use of heavy-duty excavation equipment, plus building roads where none existed, in order to get the equipment in, and building facilities for the workers and . . .

Well, that seemed no way to reduce power costs.

Not everyone who knew about it agreed with the idea of sinking radioactive wastes into the Antarctic ice mantle. Some strenuously disagreed:

I had suggested that radioactive waste be sent back to the Sun from which it originally came. My idea was that "garbage rockets" be designed which would fly into the Sun, not just into orbit. Since our Sun star is the original atomic furnace, it seems logical to return the waste material there for genuine recycling. There is literally no way we can really dispose of the stuff on Earth.
—John Sternig, Chicago, Ill. *Bulletin of the Atomic Scientists*, April, 1973.

Perhaps Antarctica as an aerially supported atomic age graveyard was not so farfetched after all. It had, as a scheme, another important advantage. Antarctica comes as close to being politically "internationalized" as any large area on earth. It should be possible to arrange for non-ideological agreements for the storage of atomic wastes from all the countries producing them, with each country paying a share of the overall cost of burying them, proportional to its use of the service.

What the effect of adding this long-term "heat sink" to the Antarctic ice cap might be, no one really seemed to know. But a pilot project might help to find out.

There is at least one potential danger in the proposal of Zeller, Saunders to use the bottom of the East Antarctic Ice Sheet as a depository for radioactive wastes. The heat from the canisters that contain the wastes may trigger a set of events that result in the elevation of the temperature to the melting point over a major fraction of the bottom surface of the ice sheet . . . Moreover, the ice sheet will be able to slide over its bed—and pulverize the canisters as it does so . . . once the bottom surface is at the melting point.
—WEERTMAN, J., "Effect of a Basal Water Layer on the Dimensions of Ice Sheets," *Journal of Glaciology*, 6 (1966). As recounted in *Science and Public Affairs*, April 1973.

The biosphere must be protected from these (atomic waste) substances for 250,000 years. Now I submit that is a very long time. In fact, the mind boggles, the blood curdles and the hair curls at the prospect of storing anything for that amount of time (except for perhaps granite). . . . We should ponder on the magnitude of 250,000 years. I submit that the only sane solution to the problem of the "disposal" of radioactive garbage is to stop producing it —right now.
—JOHN SIBERT, Fisheries Research Board of Canada, Nanaimo, B.C., in *Science and Public Affairs*, April, 1973.

In addition to its possible future use as the world's cryogenic, medical and genetic library/laboratory, cryobiotic cemetery for people who wanted to "come back," and

This land was last discovered; why? A ghost land, a continent of mystery, the very pole disconcerted the magnetic needle so that ships went astray, ice, fog and storm bound the seas, a horrid destiny in the Abrolhos, in the Philippines, in the Tasman Sea, in the Southern Ocean, all protected the malign and bitter genius of this waste land. Its heart is made of salt: it suddenly oozes from its burning pores, gold which will destroy men in greed, but not water to give them drink. Jealous land! Ravishers overbold! Bitter dilemma! And lost legion! Our land should never have been won.

Christina Stead, *Seven Poor Men of Sydney*, Sydney, 1965

Alcheringa is this Land's very soul, its bold and subtle essences imbue Australian scenes forever, constitute a bright allure and stern hypnotic power: it is the breath of sacred Yesterday, with import for Today and Tomorrow.

—T. INGLIS MOORE: *Social Patterns in Australian Literature*, Angus and Robertson, Pty. Ltd. Sydney, 1971

Painting by
R. DRYSDALE

'Project Pollute Antarctic' ends

From ALTON BRAKESLEE, at McMurdo Station, Antarctica

WHERE MAN goes, man pollutes, and this pristine white continent has not escaped the consequences of human exploration.

But now an anti-pollution conscience is greatly diminish-

For 14 years, raw sewage has been piped into the sound, hard by the shoreline of Ross Island.

This summer season, a $US175,000 (about $A156,-250) incinerator capable of burning 600 pounds of material an hour is going into action.

Next summer a sewage treatment plant, costing $US225,000 (about $A200,-

Pollution even at the South Pole

From ALTON BRAKESLEE, of Associated Press, at McMurdo Station, Antarctica

International Cooperation

A Land Without Conflict

By David Perlman
Science Correspondent

McMurdo Station, Antarctica

Britain's Antarctic researchers felt they owed the United States some favors this year in return for the thousands of miles that American Navy planes have ferried British scientists to outposts across glaciers, mountain ranges and frozen seas.

So last month six Royal Air Force crews and two RAF Hercules planes flew here from London to launch

Raw Penguin Meat Kept Them Alive

Scott Base, Antarctica

Raw penguin meat may not be a gourmet's delight. But for an American and three New Zealanders there was not much else to eat for five days while they jumped from one crumbling ice floe to another.

Lowry said they had some food in the boat, but it soon ran out and they had to capture a penguin and eat it. The boat was abandoned when they had to jump from floe to floe as the ice broke up while lashed by waves and a southerly wind.

The men joked and sang

continent are open to free inspection by observers from signatory nations. All scientific information must be freely exchanged. Nuclear explosions and disposal of radioactive wastes are forbidden.

Five more nations have signed the treaty since then, and the agreement will come up for renewal in 1990.

Many political experts feel that despite the tremendously significant scientific research accomplished in Antarctica during the last 35 years, the treaty is the most

---

the world's atomic "garbage heap," Antarctica had a number of other possibilities of particular interest for the future Australian and for many other countries as well.

For instance, experimental nuclear plants could be built there and tried out without endangering human, animal or plant life in case something went wrong. The heat from the reactors could melt the ice for use as a coolant for the nuclear cores and recycled back into the heat sink. If nothing went wrong, the experimentally produced power could be used to support communities of scientists, researchers, construction crews and technicians working on problems that required rigidly controlled environments.

Now, what else? Why not tourism? With the establishment of Trans-Antarctic air routes, already possible with contemporary jet aircraft technology, it should be possible to develop a high-paying tourist industry. Such traffic would necessarily funnel through Australia (for refueling) and thence on to New Zealand and points as south as one could get.

One could almost see the Antarctic-Hilton rising against the skyline of McMurdo Sound. In summer, giant, nuclear-powered icebreakers, as the U.S.S.R.'s "Lenin" could provide exciting tours of the ice packs. Nuclear submarines, instead of carrying missiles, could navigate beneath

Pollution Threatens Antarctic Plants,

the ice pack, performing scientific and ecological research, carry some high paying passengers, and surface from time to time for all to see the view. Led by icebreakers, merchant ships could land personnel, supplies and fuel for coastal developments.

Such excursions would be swept, if not illuminated, by the solar wind. Now, this was not the "katabatic" wind that hurls itself down from the continental dome toward the sea at hurricane speed; sometimes as much as 150 mph (240 Km/H), interesting as these winds might be, particularly if one happened to get caught by one.

The solar wind was different. Here in Antarctica, was one of the two places in the world that it could be measured with current instruments.

The particles continuously emitted from the surface of the Sun forming its continuously expanding corona comprise a moving plasma, consisting mainly of electrons, protons and alpha-particles. This plasma draws out the surface magnetic fields of the Sun until the whole envelopes the Earth as a solar wind. The magnetic field of the Earth provides a cavity called the magnetosphere into which the majority of solar wind particles cannot enter.

It is not yet known how some of the lower energy solar wind particles enter the magnetosphere, but these particles are detected by artificial satellites and are known to precipitate in two oval belts around the auroral (or geomagnetic) poles causing the Aurora Borealis in the north. The fluctuations in the solar wind cause rapid fluctuations in the electric current systems associated with auroral ovals and also in a doughnut shaped equatorial particle belt about 12,000 (19,000 kilometres) above the Earth.

And this seemed important, if only because if there was to be life on earth, it would depend upon the solar winds. Not too much was understood about them yet, but it was known that they would determine the world's climate, and perhaps greatly influence the future genetic evolution of all existing species of animals and plants in the world.

Scientists fear for Arctic Sea ice

Scientists fear that man, voluntarily or accidentally, may melt the Arctic Sea ice, leading to irreversible climatic changes

The United Nations Educational Scientific and Cultural Organisation says in its latest bulletin that group of 30 scientists from 14 countries have called for an international agreement concerning experimentation in the Arctic.

The group met at the study singled out the Arctic ice as the feature on the earth's surface most sensitive to man-made changes. Once melting began in this area it was unlikely that it would stop, the report said.

Several proposals had already been made to eliminate the ice, one suggestion being to spread soot or black dust on the frozen sea to absorb the sun's heat and increase melting in the summer and spring.

While these were only suggestions they pointed to

Mystery Valleys

Antarctic Land Dry as a Desert

Icebergs in L. A.

By George Getze
L.A. Times Service

Santa Monica

One of Earth's truly great resources, the 10,000-year accumulation of fresh water frozen into the Antarctic ice cap, is going untapped.

It won't be neglected by eager entrepreneurs much longer if two Rand Corp. senior researchers are right. They say it is perfectly feasible to tow huge Antarctic icebergs to Southern California, Australia, Chile or other thirsty places.

It's not only physically possible, it is possible to do it cheaply enough to make the necessary planning and engineering worthwhile according to John Holt and Neill Ostrander.

In fact, they say water from icebergs could be delivered in southern California for about $50 an acre-foot, compare this to the $65 an acre-foot that California Aqueduct water is costing.

See Back Page

But despite all this, the most exciting possibility for the future of Antarctica appeared to be political. This was kind of strange, because there was almost no one there. Sure, there were some old timers: the emperor penguin, the Adelie penguin, the snow petrel (one never ran out of petrel down there), and the south polar skua, the crabtree seal, the Weddell seal, the Ross seal, the leopard seal, and the elephant seal. There also was a smattering of inland residents including sucking lice, mites, springtails, ticks, and wingless flies (how does a wingless fly fly?). And then there were the tardigrades, or water bears, whatever they were. Water bears?

The point, if any, was that the natives of Antarctica were not entitled to vote, but many nations of the world could. And therein lies a story, a future history embedded in the ice and frozen in the minds of men.

The human story of the Antarctican continent was unique in the history of mankind. For once, something political actually worked. People of many nationalities, ideologies, linguistic systems and religions got together and decided, let's stop all this nonsense and work *with* each other instead of against each other.

And so it came to pass.

Unlike the League of Nations or the United Nations, men of different persuasions found that the flapping of a flag was not as important as the exchange of ideas and experiences. The hard and brassy cacophony of the resurgent crystals was indeed, "The New World Symphony."

It had never happened on any continent before. But the feedback from the Antarctican experience *could* make it happen in other continents and cultures severed by ancient strifes, caused by men who desired power more than understanding; poor paranoics on the perimeter of humanity.

Encircling the design makers, like the animals in a Disney cartoon, stood the penguins and the seals, the skua and the petrels; the silent majority awaiting the turn of man's mind in its slow evolution to maturity.

Meanwhile, the great whales arched off-coast in silent splendor, observing from far-out bleachers the drama being enacted on the giant stage of Antarctica.

Here, on this white and icy stage was being performed what could be the last act of the world. Like all last acts it gave not resolution, but asked a question.

The question was "Could men ever become human?"

The silent majority could only watch— and pray.

Russians drill deep into ancient ice

MOSCOW, Monday.— Soviet scientists have drilled to 1,837 feet in the ice cover of the Antarctic, a record for glacier drilling, Tass has reported.

A study of bacteria and dust particles of earth and cosmic origin obtained from the ice core sample may give clues to the past radiation and heat condition of the earth, the agency said.

The core obtained by the Soviet scientists is more than 150 centuries old.

Professor Boris Kudryashov, a designer of the drill used in the project, believes it may be possible to penetrate through the ings will provide some clues about the formation of the South Polar continent and perhaps reveal some history of glaciation in the southern hemisphere."

Dr McGinnis said Antarctica had been explored for decades but nearly all studies had been on the surface and most drillings were only into ice-caps.

"There is no likelihood of finding oil," he said.

"There may be valuable minerals, however, but it might not be economical for commercial miners to try to remove them."

A microbiological group

Magnetic 'Racetrack' Seen as Aid to Radio

Antarctica Study May Lead to System Unaffected by Sun Storms and Blackouts

McMURDO STATION, Antarctica (AP)—Thousands of miles above the earth floats an astonishing magnetic racetrack. static or blackouts. When a flash of lightning occurs, about 10% of that energy ... tes through the

Antarctica: new anti-pollution measure to keep the ice nice

By ALTON BLAKESLEE   McMURDO SOUND

Urgent Search in Antarctic
Bagging Seals for Science

By David Perlman
Science Correspondent

McMurdo Station, Antarctica

An eight-foot-long Weddell seal gave a loud territorial grunt as Don Siniff and his graduate student deftly slipped a canvas bag over the bull's head.

Then, in calming darkness, the animal lay still while Siniff fastened a waterproof radio transmitter around its left rear flipper.

seal hunting is about to become a reality in the ice-packed waters of Antarctica, and strict conservation rules must be based on firm scientific knowledge.

The bull with the mobile transmitter offers one route to that knowledge. As the animal swims beneath the ice and interacts with other seals — copulating, fighting, ranging far for fish — its location signals reveal unknown aspects of its life style.

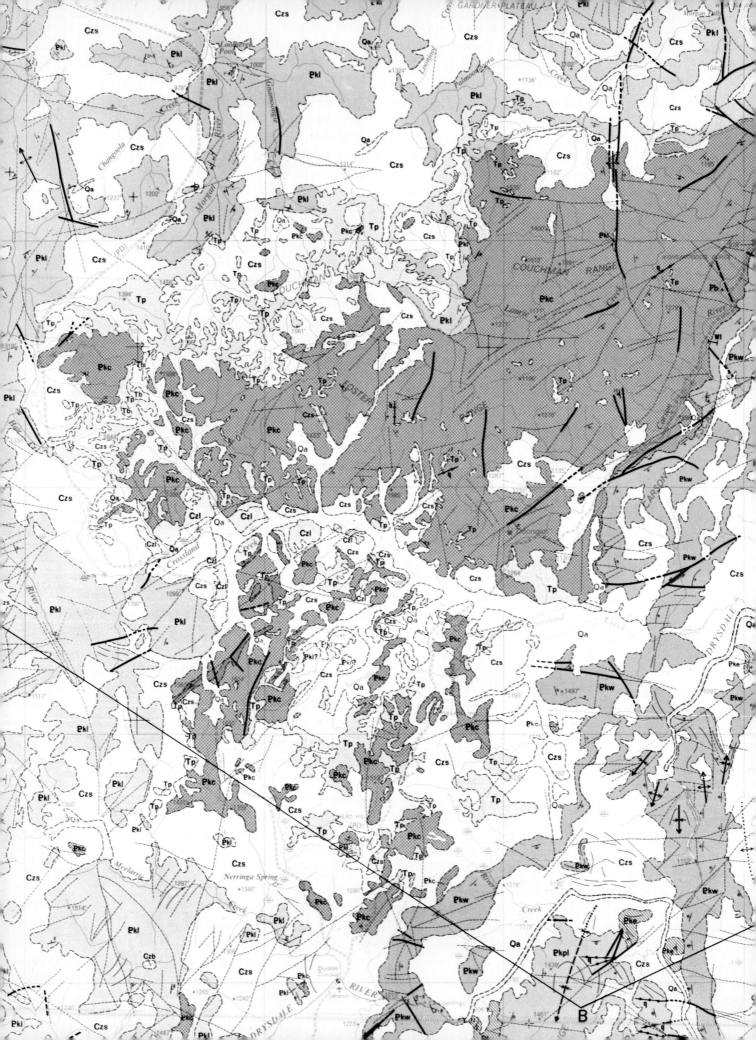

Balancing on
the balls of one's feet
in the chart room of the
Stone Raft, squinting in
the dim light of the 20th
Century, one could
just make out the
entries in the log of its
billions of years'
voyage. Someplace it
must have put on fuel.
Someplace it loaded
cargo. Some entries in
the Stone Raft's log —
and in its manifest —
might read like this:

ell, it looked like there was a pretty promising manifest; a veritable treasure chest.

There was some gold left, though not much. The gold had been spent in the 19th Century as the emotive force that catapulted the Stone Raft into the international market. There might be some more gold cached away in unexamined holds, but as one checked things in this point of time, most of it seemed to be at Kalgoorlie in Western Australia and at Tennant Creek in the Northern Territory.

With world gold prices constantly rising, it was at least possible, if not probable that, coupled with the application of more sophisticated mining equipment and techniques, some of the old mines might be started up again. The golden glitter of towns that had given up everything but the ghost might once again sparkle on the Australian landscape. All of this was conceivable by the year 2000. If it did happen, Australia would have an important, even if relatively modest, leverage in world trade markets.

Silver, zinc and lead filled several great holds. Mt. Isa and Broken Hill ranked among richest mines on earth, with a future expectancy of commercially profitable mining for at least another half a century. The constant growth of photography and electronic devices argued well for an expanding future market for silver, and the spread of nuclear power generating plants seemed to point to a growing future market for lead (used in shielding and radioactive waste disposal systems), and zinc would continue to find new markets as world housing needs increased. Altogether, there seemed to be a silver lining in the shadow of those deep holds.

There was copper gleaming there, too—at Mt. Isa—in enormous quantities. Some poking around suggested there might be equally rich mountains of copper, just waiting to be found. It was as if the congealed blood of civilizations long ago would run in rivulets down the veins of the world. A pretty nice piece of cargo for the future.

Nickel: Kambalda Western Australia 1966

Although it had been stored there in hold all the time, an entry in the Stone Raft's log shows that nickel was not discovered until 1966. Up until then, nobody even knew that this treasure was aboard in high grade, commercially exploitable quantities.

For the Australians, the historic "gold fever" was reincarnated with "nickel fever." Small deposits of the valuable metal had been producing since 1913, but the product had only been used in a limited way locally. It was the big strike at Kambalda, 35 miles south of Kalgoorlie, that set off the great nickel speculation bushfire of the late 1960's and early 1970's.

Despite the fact that some of the nickel "discoveries" turned out to be deposits of press release paper, there did appear to be a huge cargo of the real metal aboard. By 1970, estimated commercially profitable reserves totaled about 500 million tons, which if dug up and refined, could supply a substantial part of the world's estimated nickel needs at least until the year 2000. (Only four years after the Kambalda discovery, Australia ranked sixth among all the world's producers of nickel; a remarkable accomplishment.)

The Kambalda nickel discovery sparked off an exploration boom rivalling the gold rush to nearby Kalgoorlie 70 years earlier. While several more discoveries have been made in the same area, the field of exploration has spread not only to cover the whole of the Eastern Goldfields, from Norseman to Meekatharra, but also to the Pilbara area and several other prospective areas throughout Australia.
—DR. Z. KALIX, *Mineral Industry,* Department of National Development, Canberra, 1969.

The nickel ore so far discovered runs from about 4% nickel content down to 0.6%, with an average of about 2.5%, which was considered pretty good by world standards. The ore value in some places could be increased by separating other metals associated with the nickel itself; traveling companions like copper and cobalt.

It (the discovery of nickel at Kambalda) was enough to trigger off an exploration boom in "the West" which rivals the activity that followed the discovery of gold at Kalgoorlie in 1892. Established Australian mining companies, companies from overseas and a flood of newly floated prospecting companies have swarmed to the nickel country, pegging likely ground as quickly as maps and scanty geological information permit . . . Indeed, investing (or gambling) on nickel stocks has become a favorite Australian pastime, with the result that many fortunes have been made and lost in recent years in a stock market boom unmatched in Australian history since the Silver boom of the 1880's.
—IAN COGHILL, *Australia's Mineral Wealth,* Sorrett Publishing Pty. Ltd., Melbourne, 1971.

No proven or potential reserves estimates have been released by Broken Hill Proprietary Company, but it is generally thought that the Groote Eylandt manganese deposit must rank as one of the best in the world, especially in view of its quality, ease of extraction and proximity to deep water.
—IAN COGHILL, *Australia's Mineral Wealth,* Sorrett Publishing Pty. Ltd., Melbourne, 1971.

Nevertheless, one thought that what Australia really needed was "a good 5% nickel." (To paraphrase an old American political slogan, "What this country needs is a good 5¢ cigar.")

Since nickel was an essential alloying ingredient for some high-grade steels (as well as many other uses), it seemed probable that as Australia's iron exports expanded, the market for nickel would, too. As a profitable cargo for delivery to the world's markets of the future, nickel took on all the gleam of silver and the glitter of long-ago gold.

Manganese Groote Eylandt 1907

This was a very valuable bit of cargo. But despite that its jet-black color made it easily recognizable, explorers, prospectors and geologists had largely overlooked it. Probably this was because it was hidden under a relatively thin layer of topsoil, and, in any event most of the people out fossicking were looking for something that glittered like gold or galena, and not some dumb old black rock. An entry in the log showed that manganese had been found in small, but commercial quantities since 1882 (mostly from a place called Horseshoe, 80 miles from Meekatharra, wherever that was) up until the 1960's, but it was not nearly enough for Australia's needs.

Then in the early '60's, large deposits—ranked among the largest and best quality in the world—were discovered on Groote Eylandt, on the Northern Territory side of the Gulf of Carpentaria.

Production of manganese ore increased to 754,000 tons in 1968, with 600,000 tons coming from Groote Eylandt, in the Northern Territory, and the remainder from several smaller mines in the Peak Hill and Pilbara districts of Western Australia . . . Groote Eylandt supplies most of Australia's metallurgical manganese and the balance of production is exported.
—KALIX, DR. Z., Mineral Resources Branch, *Mineral Industry*, Geographic Section, Atlas of Australian Resources Department of National Development, Canberra, 1969.

The realization in the early 1960's that Australia had at Groote Eylandt, a large, highly accessible deposit of high-grade manganese ore, was to change the manganese situation completely. As with bauxite at the same time, a deficit situation was suddenly transformed into one of abundance, and the prospect of a profitable export business was soon apparent.
—IAN COGHILL, *Australia's Mineral Wealth*, Sorrett Publishing Pty. Ltd., Melbourne, 1972.

The first off-loading from Groote Eylandt began in the spring of 1966; for the steel making countries that drank up manganese, this was a vintage year.

Manganese was an essential alloy of high-grade steel, and it had—as profitable ports of delivery—Japan, Europe and the United States, none of which had been able to unearth very much high-grade manganese of their own. Yet it was an essential ingredient of late 20th Century industrial technology.

Future deliveries would be dependent on the expansion of the world market for high-grade steel, and this expansion seemed assured, given a growing world population, increasing industrialization, and all those mountains of iron ore along the northeastern coast of Australia.

It looked like a groote opportunity for the next thirty years and more.

Byron Bay
N.S.W.
1935

Cruising real close to the shore, swaying slightly in the jade-green, reef-subdued waves, one could see long, dark patches on the bone-gleaming beaches. From this distance, bobbing offshore, the patterns looked something like the serigraphs one might see in a modern art studio.

These strange dark-sand configurations stretched for miles. One would send a party boat ashore to examine this stain on the gleaming teeth that bit the sea. One scooped up a handful of this strange stuff and found trembling there a treasure almost beyond belief. The hastily gathered sample weighed heavily in one's hand, much heavier than the white sands that surrounded it. Must be something there.

Australia is the world's leading producer of mineral sands producing annually almost 95 per cent of all rutile, about 80 per cent of all zircon, about one-quarter of all ilmenite and monzonite production. As only a small fraction of this production is consumed within Australia . . . the mineral sands industry is an important foreign exchange earner . . .
—IAN COGHILL, *Australia's Mineral Wealth*, Sorrett Publishing, Melbourne, 1971.

Later on, the odd-colored grains were to be given some mighty fancy names: rutile, zircon, ilmenite, garnet, monzonite, leucoxine . . .

One held not only a handful of semi-precious minerals scooped at random from the dark streaks on the beach, but a mouthful of unknown words, as well. The ship's library gave a few definitions. One thumbed the well-worn pages and found:

Rutile: the lustrous red, reddish brown or black form of titanium dioxide, TiO_2, used as a gemstone, as a source of titanium, and in paints and fillers.

Zircon: a brown to colorless mineral, essentially $ZrSiO_4$, which is heated, cut and polished to form a brilliant blue-white gem . . . It is also used as a furnace refractory and in ceramics, in the construction of nuclear reactors, in alloys for hardness, in vacuum tubes to remove oxygen, in high-intensity electric arc lamps, and in surgical instruments.

Ilmenite: a lustrous black-to-brownish titanium ore, essentially $FeTiO_3$. In various forms used as a transducer, for smoke screens and in sky-writing, as a catalyst in the petroleum industry, for waterproofing fibers, air and spacecraft construction, naval ships, guided missiles and lightweight armour plate for tanks.

Garnet: a silicate mineral colored red, brown, black, green, yellow or white, used as gemstones and for sandpaper. (Strangely, the name comes from its most common color—red—and derives from the French word *Pomegranate*; literally, an apple containing many seeds. That is where the word "granite" comes from also, derived from the original "gran," meaning many small particles. Small world of words, indeed!)

Monzonite: an igneous rock composed chiefly of plagioclase and orthoclase, with small amounts of other minerals. Used chiefly in crossword puzzles.

Leucoxine: an opaque, lightish mineral formed as a decomposition product of ilmenite; believed to be a variety of sphene. Sphene? Well, now, that's a titanium ore, chiefly used as a gemstone. Sphene comes from the ancient Greek, meaning wedge . . .

To hell with it.

Almost as exotic as the sand minerals themselves were the names of the places where they were found. "The heavy mineral deposits are distributed along the beach of Geographe Bay from Bunburry to Cape Naturaliste," and on "a higher shoreline north and south of Yoganup, which is south of Capel, and on the Recent beaches at Wonnerup."

Most Australian punters are most likely to find that they have bet on a Wonnerup.

Standing there, feet spread to counter the sway and bob of the wayward waves, one hand full of sand, the other impregnated by a mouldy book, one might scan the area behind the beach. Mostly weather-worn hills crouching in time-rounded shapes like sleeping cats.

Suppose that over the millenia, the hard rains had executed a kind of Chinese torture on the bare backbone of the granitic and basaltic that formed the skin of the earth. Suppose that the raindrops displaced grains of the exposed rock and that they tumbled down into rivulets and streams and rivers and willy-nilly were swept down to the coast.

They met the ocean there; the momentum of their headlong trip was slowed by the incoming tides and the cliff-like seas that avalanched like jade walls; Jericho incessant. The heavier grains of sand, now deprived of transportation, went into parking lots, while the lighter particles were wafted out to fall like snow on the ramparts of the reef.

One could, in this moment of fantasy, imagine that, left behind, the heavier particles formed communities; great dark stains on the sea-driven beach.

Again and again. The great storms came in. The receding waves carried away the

Mining: the mighty gamble Part 1

Great two-up game falters

At first there was gold

Although copper is now the most important mineral mined at Tennant Creek it was gold which engendered initial interest. The first recorded discovery of gold in the area was made in 1864 by a South Australian geologist named Brown, who accompanied a gold-seeking expedition from Adelaide.

More promising gold shows near the Adelaide River in the Northern Territory diverted the attention of prospectors and it was not until the 1920's that Tennant Creek's gold again attracted interest. Alert Aborigines in the area are reported to have triggered off the interest when they brought some rock samples to an Overland Telegraph officer at Tennant Creek.

Assays were good and Tennant Creek became a target for the eager groups of gold prospectors of the era. Rapidly new names appeared on the map: Cat's Whiskers, Golden Chance, Black Eye, Hidden Mystery, Shamrock and Great Western, to name a few.

In 1931 payable gold was discovered. By 1935 140 leases were being worked by gougers but many proved unsuccessful. Two who were lucky were Jack Noble and Billy Weaber. They

discovered Noble's Nob, described as the richest gold mine for its size in the world.

Only now does Noble's Nob, worked by Australian Development Limited, appear to be close to exhaustion. It must have been intuition because Weaber was blind and Noble had sight in only one eye! Intuition or otherwise, Noble considered his find promising enough to sink a shaft by the laborious hammer and tap method in hard hematite without encountering significant values above 50 ft.

On the failure side was a former R.A.F. pilot, Sam Sumerfield, holder of British Pilot's Licence No. 3, who flew the first aircraft into Tennant Creek in 1931. He searched in vain for gold at Mary Lane and tried unsuccessfully to establish Tennant Creek's first air service.

Near Orlando mine the remains stand today of Dolly Pot Inn, believed to have been the smallest licensed premises in Australia 12 ft. by 10 ft. In a shack nearby lives pensioner Ernie Skein, last licencee of Dolly Pot Inn. He still gouges for gold.

In the 1930's there was extensive digging in the Warramunga field which contains Noble's Nob and the Peko mines. The gold won in this era was "secondary", being derived from the ironstone lodes by weathering and erosion and redeposited either in the ironstones or the adjacent sedimentary rocks at some lower depth.

Mostly as mining proceeded downwards the ore grade dropped and working became uneconomic. Eldorado, now abandoned, and Noble's Nob were the exceptions. Noble's Nob was a very deep mine by the standards of the 1930's.

The only outcropping deposit in the Warramunga field was found in 1935 by a Polish prospector, Joe Kaczensky, who named it Peko after his Pekingese dog. It is the mine which since has produced copper, gold, bismuth and silver.

Peko mine has served as a hub for Tennant Creek mining development and now there are five producing mines Peko, Orlando, Juno, Noble's Nob, and Ivanhoe and two others almost ready for production Gecko and Warrego.

Coober Pedy–World Opal Capital
(where a comfortable home is a hole in the ground)

lighter grains, leaving behind the heavy ones. The configuration in its density was not unlike colonies of humans along the coasts of the world.

These colonies of dark grains grew more and more densely concentrated. Until one day a monster that looked like a bulldozer came along, scooped them up, dumped them into a truck. And then the hard and heavy little grains went to the great ovens, to be transformed, after many a journey, into paints, paper additives, and strange flying things that took them to the moon and beyond. It was a long journey from the mountains to the sea; an even longer one to the moon, but if there was anything these little hard-shelled creatures had, it was time.

Meanwhile, at least while that was going on—the bulldozer was a sort of frightening monster to disturb one's billion year dreams. Romping and chomping, chewing and spitting, under the direction of a goggle-eyed, hard-helmeted creature from outer time, the steel beast marched inexorably down the beach, gulping up huge quantities of sand with a single bite; spewing out the ones too light to keep, and storing the heavy grains in its belly. A hard cud to chew on.

Hard as the times might be, there was something rather interesting in the process that augured well for helping to solve some of the problems of old goggle-eye. For instance, if the heavy sands could be separated from the light ones, simply because of the difference in their comparative gravities, then why couldn't this be applied to other residues as well?

Other residues included abandoned automobiles and demolished buildings, discarded household effects and all of the detritus of technological civilization.

One could grind them all up into small grains (hence "granitic"), separate them by centrifugal, flotational, or magnetic forces or whatever, and recycle them. Such a scheme would cut down considerably on the waste that littered the landscape. It could reduce the exploitation of limited natural resources, and would be a kind of happy—and possibly profitable—reincarnation for all the material things on earth.

This was a rather deep thought about a little grain of sand, with the bulldozer rumbling toward it. But grains of sand had time to think about things. Old goggle-eyes, pulling the levers that directed his snorting steel beast, didn't have the time to think about much of anything. Perhaps, soon, he would. He, too, was washed by the storms and tides of time. Being of light weight, he might well be washed out to the reefs of eternity. The little sand pebbles would remain pretty much the same, slowly acting out their billion-year role in the comedy of the world.

But in the here and now, the colorful little seeds had to remember that they were themselves just transient residents of a much larger community, made up of sand dunes and salt grass, and all the creeping, scuttling, hopping, slithering, flying creatures in the same area. And they were all on a different time trip than the little grains.

What would happen to them; the dunes, the grass and the little people—when the monster scooped them up and gulped them down, spit out the sand and rumbled on its wayward way?

One thing seemed sure; goggle-eyes didn't know. What could not be digested was thrown back and formed new dunes. But something was missing; the vegetation and all the little people were gone with the wind. It had taken them millions of years to get there and to undertake their complex rituals of life in the storm of wind and waves, of sun and sand. How long would it take them to come back? Nobody knew—or seemingly cared.

Some ecologists and environmentalists did, but their voices could scarcely be heard over the roar of the bulldozer's engines. Perhaps, in time the voices crying in the wilderness would be heard. But by then, it might be too late.

Meanwhile, a handful of sand gave one something to think about, did it not?

Uranium
Rum Jungle
1869

A part of the ghost of the world's future slept for billions of years in nondescript rocks—nondescript in the eyes of the prospectors of those days. Except for a few greasy green samples there was nothing but little old black rocks (pitchblende). They did not have the glitter of gold, the sibilance of silver, colour of copper, nor the ring of iron.

The ghost of things to come spoke so softly that his voice was not heard for 80 years after the discovery of uranium by curious prospectors at Rum Jungle in 1869.

It took a little formula from Einstein, so elegant in its simplicity as to be unbelievable, the Manhattan project in the U.S., so huge as to be unbelievable, and the horror of Hiroshima and Nagasaki to turn those little black rocks into equally unbelievable mineral wealth.

The increasing application of specialized techniques such as geophysics, geochemistry, geomorphology and palaeo-geography, have given a new impetus to mineral exploration in the last decade or so, and give hope that discoveries of major deposits will continue.
—MINERAL DEPOSITS, Department of National Development, Canberra, 1970.

The ghost of the atomic future walked upon the midnight of the world in such unlikely places as Rum Jungle, Nabarlek, Pandanas Creek, Jim Creek, South Alligator River, and Mary Kathleen.

Mary Kathleen? Yes, Mary Kathleen. One could remember how that anima of the rocky ghost was invoked. Here was the story of that invocation as told by the prospector who found her sleeping in a dry stream bed: She woke to the sound of a Geiger counter to the morning (hopefully not mourning) of the 21st Century. It came about this way:

"Although other prospectors had maps, we had local knowledge. We knew where to go. But we didn't like the country where our discovery was made. We didn't think it had any uranium in it. You can see how a man can go wrong.

"It all started on 3rd July (1954) when . . . we went prospecting. The jeep stopped in a creek bed, and while the others were getting her out Norman McConachy picked up a stone—what we call a floater (a loose rock as distinct from an outcrop), with his geiger. The count was 2,500 and it was real hot . . . Then Norman found another stone in the creek and it was real hot, too.

"Norm and the boys stopped looking that afternoon when it got dark, but three days later . . . we all went out to try to find where those hot stones came from . . . We followed up the creek till we found what we call a greenstone. It was washed and bare. There was no count, but the background count was high.

"We went slowly up the creek and in a bend we found two or three more hot stones. Then a little further up we found one that was really hot.

"It was the size of your head, and the count was 10,000. A count that high is rare. I wrapped that rock up in my coat because I reckoned we really had it.

"Then we noticed that nature had done a remarkable thing for us. There had been a landslide on the hill above the creek. It had bared the centre of the earth and had made a natural open cut.

"Three thousand is regarded as a very good count, but when we put the geigers on to the open cut they buzzed contin-uously and recorded counts that seemed fantastic. The highest count we got was 48,000 which is almost unbelievable. None of us could realize that we had made such a find. But we pegged an area two miles long by a half a mile wide."

—As told to Ronald McKie and quoted in Raggat H. G., *Mountains of Ore*, Lansdowne Press, Melbourne, 1968.

Of course, one did not know how many hot rocks were sleeping down there in the forgotten bunkers. But one did know one thing for certain; there was a lot of high grade ore down there, about a quarter of the world's known reserves, and, at least at Nabarlek, of unbelievably high uranium oxide content (540 pounds per ton, 27 percent pure) compared to a world average of no more than three pounds per ton. Any time you have a factor of more than eight times three, you have a good thing going in the economic field.

As the world's technologically developed countries shifted from fossil fuels, such as coal and petroleum, for electrical energy toward nuclear plants, the uranium in the bunkers became more and more valuable.

The Japanese market alone looks extremely attractive in the middle and longterm for uranium producers. One of the advantages of nuclear electricity generation in a highly industrialized country is that it is virtually pollution free. Already oil-fired generating stations have been refused permits to build in several areas of Japan. As coal-fired furnaces produce more pollutants than oil, and as Japan has little hydro-electric potential, nuclear generation offers the only feasible alternative.
—IAN COGHILL: *Australia's Mineral Wealth*, Sorret Publishing, Melbourne, 1971.

Thus, the first port of call for that partic-ular cargo would be Japan. The Japanese Atomic Energy Conference in 1970 had

83

Countdown for uranium

U.S. feels pinch of too much too soon

Uranium diplomacy— Australia is ready to play

Uranium lift 'not as far off as many experts predict'

forecast an expected demand for uranium oxide over the subsequent twenty years of about 200,000 tons. This alone would eat up Mary Kathleen, Nabarlek, and all the others in a single gulp in time.

Change course for Japan and set the chronometer for the year 2000!

Bauxite Weipa, N.Q. 1955

"On the 16th July, on the edge of a high tableland overlooking the head waters of the Embley River, I found an outcrop of pisolitic bauxite. The bauxite outcropped as boulders and blocks up to three feet thick. There appeared to be about half a square mile of it. I collected three samples and returned to York Downs Station. That night the possibility of continuing west to the Weipa Mission was discussed with the owner of the York Downs Station, who stated that a track was known to exist between his station and the Mission. Next day I set off with a native guide. We reached the Weipa Mission Station that night after having been bogged in two tidal creeks on the way. En route, we passed over at least six miles of pisolitic material which I sampled at approximately one mile intervals. By this time I was beginning to realise just how extensive the bauxite deposit was and its possible economic significance.

"Next morning, standing in front of the Mission House, I realised that red cliffs extended across the Embley River south of the Mission. This indicated a possible extension south along the coast. As no boat was available at the Mission, I returned to Coen and then south to Melbourne. The samples collected on the trip were forwarded to Bell Bay for analysis and the results indicated that the Weipa deposit could be of commercial interest.

"It was decided that I should return to the area and try to cover as much of the coastal area as possible by whatever means of transport I could obtain in the area. I arrived at Coen by air on October 5th and found that I could hire a Land Rover and a 9 ft. dinghy with outboard motor from the owner of Silver Plains cattle station.

"We arrived at Weipa on 9th October. I obtained the services of an old native named Matthew and we set off next day in the dinghy to examine the cliffs across the Embley River and continued along the south bank of the estuary toward Urquhart Point on Albatross Bay. Choppy waves swamped the outboard motor and, while trying to clear the motor, the throttle dropped overboard in 12 feet of muddy water. We rowed back across the estuary to the Mission and that evening we checked the few available truck parts about the Mission but could not find a suitable part. The trip down the coast seemed now to be out of the question. However, we had another look at the outboard carburettor and ended up making a throttle out of the end of a native spear handle.

The great potential of the bauxite deposits around the Gulf of Carpentaria and in the Darling Range of Western Australia has only been realized in the past 15 years . . . The Weipa deposits are probably the largest single occurrence of bauxite in the world — economic-grade bauxite covers at least 200 square miles between Vrilya Point and Archer Bay, and reserves of bauxite probably exceed 3,000 million tons. The bauxite forms a flat-lying surface deposit ranging in thickness from a few feet to 30 feet.
—I. R. McLEOD and Y. MIEZITIS, Geological Branch, Bureau of Mineral Resources, Geology and Geophysics, Canberra, 1970.

"On the 11th October we set off again but, because of the small size of the dinghy, it was decided that all available space would have to be used for fuel and our bedrolls. For food we decided we could mostly live off the land. We landed at Urquhart Point and looking across Albatross Bay towards Duyfken Point, which appeared to be relatively high ground and hence possibly bauxite-bearing. I decided to take a look at Duyfken Point before setting off south along the coast. After a very rough journey we sheltered that evening in a small cove, just east of Duyfken Point. Next day, when the sea had calmed, we headed around Duyfken Point and along the coast for five miles. As bauxite outcrops were scarce and the heavy breakers along the main coast made landing difficult, I decided to head south. With our fingers crossed we headed across Albatross Bay once again and made the coast just south of Urquhart Point without too much trouble. That night we camped beneath a tree on the beach ten miles south of Urquhart Point.

The Chairman of Consolidated Zinc, M. A. E. Mawby (now Sir Maurice) had not forgotten his geology. In June 1953 he issued the following memorandum to his executive staff:
"Please issue instructions to all field geologists that, apart from the search for base metals, they should also keep an eye open for possible deposits of other minerals, particularly phosphate and bauxite—which may occur in many places in the Northern Territory and, possibly, Cape York Peninsula . . ."
Two years later (October 1955) the company's chief field geologist, Harry Evans, recorded in his notebook:
"I keep thinking that if all this is bauxite, then there must be something the matter with it . . ."
But it was bauxite, about one-quarter of the world's known high-grade reserves in one massive deposit!
—IAN COGHILL, Australia's Mineral Wealth, Sorrett Publishing Pty. Ltd., Melbourne, 1971.

"From there we continued 30 miles south to Pera Head in the open sea, landing at intervals along the coast to sample the bauxite cliffs. The mornings were generally calm but by 2 o'clock each day the westerly winds blew steadily and rough seas were quite troublesome. The main difficulty for us was that the improvised spear handle throttle could only be adjusted for a fixed speed and the only way to stop the motor was to shut off the petrol. Most times, the dinghy and its contents were swamped during landing.

As for production (of bauxite from Comalco's Weipa properties), the long-term contracts . . . are remarkable . . . Comalco was committed to supply 194 million tons between 1970 and 1997 with customers having the right to take a further 176 million tons to the year 2041 if they wish. Contracts being negotiated (as of February 1971) involved another 121 million tons between 1971 and 2008 with options running into a further 49 million tons. The mind boggles at the immensity of such orders.
—IAN COGHILL, Australia's Mineral Wealth, Sorrett Publishing Pty. Ltd., Melbourne, 1971.

"As the journey down the coast revealed miles of bauxite cliffs, I kept thinking that, if all this was bauxite, then there must be something the matter with it, otherwise it would have been discovered and appreciated long ago. After reaching Pera Head, we decided to go another ten miles down to Norman Creek, where we turned back to Weipa as fuel supplies were running low. During this journey I examined 52 miles of coastline and travelled 180 miles in a 9 foot dinghy with outboard motor."

—(As related by H. J. Evans in *Weipa—How the Bauxite was Finally Recognised.*)

So that, according to an entry in the Stone Raft's log, was how it all began.

Its end was not in sight.

There were, at Weipa alone, proved out reserves of bauxite that could satisfy the world's aluminum needs for centuries. There were a geologically proven 516 million tons of commercial grade bauxite there, with the possibility that the ultimate deposit might be well over 2,000 million tons.

But Weipa was only one, even if it was the largest, of the proven bauxite deposits on the Stone Raft. There also were vast deposits at Gove, the Darling Range and on the Mitchell Plateau in the Kimberley Range.

When one added up the already proven bauxite resources, they came out to more than 3,700 million tons. Enough to help carry men to the Moon and back; ultimately to Mars and to Jupiter, to Saturn and Uranus and Pluto. Also enough to build all the rapid transit systems in the world. Enough to build all the skyscrapers to stand like monuments against the evening sky for all the cities of which man could dream.

In that layer of yellow or red colored bauxite was the foundation metal of what was, perhaps too optimistically, called the "Space Age"—which had only begun.

There would be many ports of call for this load of bauxite and its derivatives in the years to come. Here was a silvery-colored river that flew the wings of the future. It was born of plain old red dirt, and that red dirt was perhaps the most precious cargo aboard the Stone Raft. Its principal destination was the 21st Century, and a world market that was growing wings.

There was a lot of deck cargo; most of it timber. These were dry white bones of dead eucalypts, cut down to clear pastures and to fence paddocks for sheep, more sheep, ever more sheep. In traditional English and European style, the Australians had almost always thought of timber as an enemy to be killed and that its carcass could then be sawn into shapes that could be pieced together to make buildings. But the eucalypts were not much good for that. So the glow of their burning became Australia's fire by night; giant pyres of windrows on the rims of the newly created paddocks.

But then a new game was introduced.

It was discovered that if the eucalypt trunks and branches and twigs could be ground up into chips, the chips were an admirable raw material for paper, paper-board, fibreboard and particle board—all products increasingly in demand in a world characterized by exploding population and technologically "developing" countries.

The first port of delivery for this new ("new" for Australia, at least) product was Japan because little in the way of forest products remained and there was a growing population and an urgent need for housing. Contracts for wood chips from the Australian eucalypts already totaled $400 million:

The role of Japan is crucial to the development of the wood-chip industry in Australia. Her consumption of paper products is increasing rapidly and at the present per capita level of about 170 lbs. has obvious scope for future expansion. Indeed, she seeks supplies of raw materials from all round the Pacific to feed her pulp mills, which cannot be supplied from inside Japan.
—*Rural Research in CSIRO No. 73*, September 1971

Now, the comforting thing about this particular kind of cargo was that, unlike bauxite, or iron, or copper, coal or silver, the wood chips were a constantly renewable product.

Under suitable conditions, eucalypts could grow ten feet in height and an inch in diameter every year, thus a marketable product (in the form of wood chips) could be produced every 12 to 15 years. Another possibility that was being examined was that the coppice (i.e. the brush that grows quite rapidly from the stumps of previously cut trees) could form a pulp for fine grain paper.

If this turned out to be feasible, it had two advantages. In the first place the coppice would grow much faster than a tree, and it could be mechanically harvested.

Beyond doubt, the production of wood chips from coppice-grown eucalypts shows promise. Furthermore, the approach harmonizes with the trend in forestry towards full mechanization. The machine needed to harvest small stems should be cheaper to build, lighter, and capable of operating on a wider variety of terrain than those required to harvest conventional pulpwood. Moreover, prospects of higher yields exist, and the short rotation overcomes, in principle, one of the main bugbears of forestry ventures — that is, the long wait before any returns on capital invested are forthcoming.
— "Growing Eucalypts for Wood Chips," *Rural Research in CSIRO, No. 73,* September, 1971

Somehow, one thought, that deck cargo of eucalypts might be one of the most promising and profitable aboard — it could be good for a thousand years; certainly until the year 2000.

Pilbara Western Australia December, 1961

For most of its long voyage, it appeared that the great Stone Raft was suffering, or certainly would suffer in a technological age from a deficiency of iron. The ship's doctor had, in 1938, decreed that export of iron ore overseas was prohibited. This mandate kept anyone from looking for iron, since there was no money to be had from finding it, and Australia itself used precious little.

Then in 1960, it was decided that the patient could cure itself, and that maybe there was, after all, sufficient iron hidden there someplace. Now that there could legally be a potential export market, exploration began. The results exceeded the fondest dreams of those who poke about looking for what they do not know in the mystery one called the world.

There are untold millions of tons of iron ore in the Pilbara deposits. I think this is one of the most massive orebodies in the world. There are mountains of ore . . . It is like trying to calculate how much air there is.
— TOM PRICE, Vice President of Kaiser Steel Corporation, *Daily News,* March, 1962.

One of the crew members, an old-timer, outback-type stockraiser, named Lang Hancock, made the discovery (which Tom Price later confirmed) in November, 1962. His historic entry in the Raft's log said:

"In November, 1952, while flying south to Perth, storm clouds forced me to fly lower and lower . . .

"At the time, I was over the source of the Turner River. I knew it ran into the Ashburton clear through the ranges. The best thing to do was to follow the Turner at treetop level. The river went through a deep gorge. Its sheer walls were 200 feet high. They appeared to be iron. This was the first time I had been close to this inaccessible country, though I had frequently flown it at much greater altitude . . .

"The cliffs of the gorge absorbed my interest so much that I resolved to return in good weather and examine them more carefully . . . I returned in April and began an aerial survey of the iron ore area. After making several trips, I finally found a place to land in 1953. I took samples, made quantity estimates, and realized that this was a major discovery . . . Nothing could be done with it in view of the State Government's blanket over all iron ore in Western Australia." As quoted in the *Daily News,* Perth, March, 1961.

Stone Raft's passenger, Tom Price (a vice president of Kaiser Steel Corporation), did not discover the iron ore; Hancock did. What Tom Price did was to make available the extra dimension that Hancock could not. Tom Price could raise the money. He did it through a combine that became known as Conzinc Rio Tinto. The money was used to finance the mining operation, the railroad to carry the extracted ore some 224 miles to the coast, build a deep water port for giant ore carriers, and a community at Dampier that would provide decent, even comfortable, living for workers and their families in one of the most desolate places in the world. He also knew that Japan was ravenous for virtually unlimited supplies of high grade iron ore.

It was Tom Price who put the pieces of the iron jigsaw puzzle together; the pieces were joined together by silver and gold, and Tom knew how to find that.

One of the crew, R. T. Madigan, who was managing-director of Hamersley Iron, summed it up this way:

"The days are gone when two or three million tons of annual ore production constituted a good operation and a good profit. The ore producer must think and plan in terms of 15 million, or even 20 million tons of annual production. Only at this level . . . are ports and railways extensively used. It is not the method of pit operation nor the grade of ore which dominate strategic planning. It is the length of railway track which must be constructed to the townships which must be provided, the port and harbour dredging, and the provision and reticulation of power and water." (That is what R. T. Madigan had said at the National Convention on Management Accountants in the Mining Industry, October, 1969.)

It was the same old story aboard the Raft, and most other vessels sailing the global sea. A deck hand picks up something valuable from the holds—and an officer tells him what he can do with it.

Lang Hancock's discovery led to others. The Mt. Newman project had been proved to contain something like 1,000 million tons of high grade (64 percent) iron ore. Some estimates were that there might be as much as 2,000 million tons, right there.

The overall projections were that there were about 20,000 million tons of high grade ore (55 percent iron content). On lower grade iron ore, the projection was 150,000 to 200,000 *million* tons.

In retrospect, only a few like Tom Price could have envisioned in 1962 the magnitude of the Hamersley Iron project as it is today. Where once there was only vacant land, now there are towns and mines bringing new economic growth and wealth to Australia.
And it all happened in just a decade!
—"Hamersley: How It All Happened," *The Ingot*, December, 1972.

Apparently, The Raft had enough iron ballast to weather the economic storms of the next several centuries of the world.

Here were the skeletons of the as yet unborn skyscrapers of the future; the reinforcement bars for the concrete freeways and rapid transit systems of the 21st century; for the farm equipment that would help yield the food for a more populous and affluent world than man had ever envisaged.

Japan alone had placed contract orders for more than 250 million tons of iron ore and pellets. Here, indeed was a port of call.

And all because a little plane was forced to fly low under a cloud cover on the way to Perth! The Lord works in mysterious ways his wonders to perform—particularly in Australia.

Mount Isa
February
1923

The copper ran like the congealed blood of ancient civilizations through the gleam of galena, silver and zinc. Nobody seemed to care much about it and it got kicked around like a stepchild until World War II. Suddenly, copper became very important.

It was known already that there were substantial copper ore bodies at Mt. Isa in western North Queensland, about as far from anywhere as one could comfortably get.

Copper and lead were the first metals to be mined in Australia. The distinctive green and blue stains of carbonate of copper caught the eye of so many pastoralists and shepherds in South Australia in the 1840s that by 1850, the colony was exporting more copper than wool and wheat.
Although gold had been known to exist in Australia since 1825, none was mined until 1851.
—IAN COGHILL: *Australia's Mineral Wealth*, Sorret Publishing Pty., Ltd., October, 1971.

The discovery of copper at Mt. Isa in 1923 was so typically Australian that it was worth repeating from the Stone Raft's log. The man who wrote the entry best was Geoffrey Blainey, in "The Rush That Never Ended," a long time after the fact, but as fresh as if it had occurred tomorrow.

The discoverer's name was John Campbell Miles and his entry, as Geoffrey Blainey wrote it, went something like this:

"On a hot morning in February, 1923 he led his horses along the dry valley of the Leichhardt River, the powdered dust rising in red clouds from their tracks. In the dry riverbed the smooth trunks of the gum trees glistened ivory white and on both sides of the narrow plain the brown contours of low ranges pranced in the heat.

"Miles looked for a camping place and suddenly his pack horse smelled water and ran down to the watercourse and wallowed in the wet sand by a small waterhole.

"Miles followed her and made camp, fastening bells on the horses and filling his waterbags. He liked to prospect when he

The finality of that retreat was made clear by Bob Moody, when I met him for the first time behind his crowded bar. He and his wife, both veterans of a more recent Edie Creek rush in New Guinea, had once tried to open up some old workings a little way out of town.

"In the early days," Moody said, "there were two thousand people working around that show of mine. There's not a sign of all that life today; just an old hole in the ground. First time I drove out to look at it, we found nothing but an iron bucket with a hole in it, and an Irishman's grave.

"The going was rough, too, I can tell you. The old track had been completely obliterated. It took us eight hours in my Land-Rover to cover twenty-two miles."

Yet there have been one or two men making some sort of a living out of gold in recent years. Within the last decade the Willy Willy is said to have produced £20,000 worth, while Norman Crowther once told me he had won £8,000 in a matter of months. He showed me some of his specimens in the hotel; they were small, but solid enough nuggets.

The display prompted Moody to recall the old days when prospectors paid for their drinks in gold over the bar, taking their change in real money.

GHOST TOWNS OF AUSTRALIA
George Farwell
Rigby Ltd. 1965

R. Drysdale
Moody's Pub

was in mineralized country, so about midday he took his farrier's hammer and rode to the low ranges half a mile from the track.

"Tapping his hammer on the yellow-brown boulders on the hill, he chipped a lump of rock that was black and honey-combed and unusually heavy. He thought it must be a mineral but he did not realize it was carbonate of lead.

"Wandering through the hills that were prickly with spinifex, he saw in several places parallel bands of the same ore crossing the rock like a zebra skin. He recognized one specimen he chipped as galena, the sulphide of lead he once mined at Broken Hill. That night in his camp on the dark plain, he wondered if he had found another Broken Hill."

One could see the resemblance between Mt. Isa's discovery and that at Broken Hill. Both involved a poor "dumb" beast—a horse and a mule, respectively—most respectively who had no personal interest in silver, lead or copper, but who had bright and wide-awake human companions who did.

Well, it was a long time before anyone could brush the glitter of silver out of his eyes and take much notice of the dull, bluish copper ore, but by 1970 Mt. Isa was ranked among the largest producing copper mines in the world. Proven copper ore reserves were at 120 million tons (in 1970) and expansion and exploration plans promised to increase that figure by a large margin.

The rich red transfusion from Mt. Isa, plus the output from Mount Lyell, Iron Blow (in Tasmania), Tennant Creek, Mount Morgan, Cobar and Bougainville. Old Bogey was the richest potential of all, with a capacity of 30 million tons of copper per year, and signed contracts for 90 percent of expected production, it looked like the Stone Raft was carrying a pretty good cargo for sale in Japan, Germany and Spain.

There must have been some tropical port of call in the Stone Raft's lone voyage through time because the frozen ghosts of long departed swamps now filled the bunkers in the form of coal, and the deep tanks were brimming with the dark, energic blood of the ancient past—petroleum and its wraith-like offspring—natural gas.

Now that the Stone Raft's crew had burned off most of its eucalypts to stoke the fires of a sheep-powered economy, it depended for its motive power on the long-dead carcasses of giant ferns—on opening the gates of time to let the ghosts run exuberantly through pipes to be immolated in a final starry glory—perhaps the resurrection of their father-Sun; the waving fronds of ferns now dancing as flames.

There were an awful lot of these fire dancers aboard. The ghosts of anthracite and lignite were mostly in the stern of the Raft, where they could do the most good in shoving it along. The wraiths of oil and gas seemed to be mostly along the port side, which was good, because they were convenient for export.

Between the two of them—coal and petroleum—the Raft was well propelled on its journey in time—economically, at least.

Coal
Newcastle
1791

The discovery of coal was one of the first mineral entries in the Stone Raft's log. Since the Raft was under sail then, it didn't seem too important. About seven years later, there was another entry for coal, "Hunter River 1798."

Now there were more people and more tools, and the first commercial mining of coal began only three years later, in 1801. After that, there was no holding it and ever since then it was Australia's most important mineral product. Its overall tonnages exceeded all other mining products and, except during the Gold Rushes of the 1850s and 1900s, it employed more people than any other extractive industry. As late as 1970, some four out of every ten men engaged in mining were in coal.

This was all bituminous coal and it lay in a broad belt between the ocean and the mountains in southeastern Australia, as if it were a giant basin or series of basins in which huge quantities of Permian Age ferns were grown in some million year old terrarium.

Checking the reserve coal fuel out, it appeared there were about 5,150 million tons in the Sydney, West-Moreton-Clarence, and Bowen basins in New South Wales and Queensland. Most of the brown coal was in Victoria's Latrobe Valley.

Checking back on that Bowen Basin manifest, it seemed that perhaps somebody had not checked thoroughly enough.

The Bowen Basin, site of the Goonyella project, is a bobby pin-shaped geological feature 240 miles long and at the northern end, 40 miles wide . . . Utah Development Company said of it, "Exploration, which is still at a relatively early stage, has proved coal of all types to be in excess of 3,000 million tons at varying depths suitable for strip and deep mining techniques. Taking into account the size of the Basin and its geological structure, it is conceivable as exploration is extended and drilling proceeds to greater depths, this quantity could be enlarged to as much as 100,000 million tons.

—"COAL, the New Export Prize," *Australia Now*, published by the Australian News and Information Bureau, 1971

Somehow, this all seemed like something reminiscent of the days of the Gold Rushes. The scenery was the same, but the scenario was somewhat different, largely because of the impact of twentieth century technology and a world hunger for energy supplies, more economical means of transporting minerals in large quantities and in general, a more affluent world society that needed more and more of everything, including the coal-energy to produce it.

Australia Now caught both the similarities and the differences when it said:

"Goonyella was once a sparse plateau roamed by kangaroo and beef cattle. Today it is a scene of bustling activity. Four huge 'walking' draglines attack the overburden and 65-cubic-yard bites to expose a 23-foot seam of coal which is from 50 to 200 feet beneath the surface. Trucks of 120-ton capacity move the coal to a nearby crushing, washing, stockpiling and train loading complex.

"Hay Point, the 'push button' port for the field was unknown to most Australians until 18 months ago. There were a handful of fishing huts and the occasional tourists seeking solitude in the horseshoe-shaped bay lapped by the waters of the Great Barrier Reef."

The scene at Hay Point was something of a scenario for the year 2000. Again, picking up *Australia Now*, one could see:

"Day and night, triple-header diesel electric trains, almost a mile long and loaded with thousands of tons of newly-won coal, rumble 125 miles across flat grazing lands, over rugged ranges, through dense rain forests and lush sugar-cane fields to Hay Point, a port on Australia's east coast.

"At the automated port, fast conveyors rush the coal into bulk carriers of up to 100,000 tons which will steam out to Japanese and European ports."

There did not seem to be much use for people there and yet, apparently, there was.

". . . a 28-year-old mining engineer from Minneapolis, his wife and three young children, are among the Americans at Moranbah. They have a four-bedroom tropical home, air-conditioned against the 115 degree midsummer heat. Outside, tall native gum trees provide dappled shade.

"Frankly, I'm not looking forward to going home two years from now," he said. "We are much happier here than in any other city. There are no traffic lights, no traffic jams. Time does not seem to be so important."

This was a different world than was earlier expressed: "Find it, take it, and get out fast," or "If I could make a stake, and get out of this bloody place, I'd outrun every 'roo in the country."

They'd been saying that for 200 years, but some of them stayed. Perhaps now it was a bit easier.

It had been reckoned that by 1970, some 98.6 percent of all coal production in Australia was from fully mechanized mines, 87 percent of which was gained from "continuous miners." Like a species of gigantic mechanical moles, they burrowed through the everlasting night of the tunnels, devouring the tombs of ancient ferns.

Assuming that they maintained the estimated rate of 85 million tons per year, the mechanical moles would still be at it for at least another 300 years.

Some junior officer whose job was to keep tabs on this sort of activity aboard the Raft reckoned that "due to mechanization, output per man-shift had risen from three tons in 1950 to ten tons in 1970 in underground mining and from eight tons in 1950 to 32 tons in 1970 in open-cut mines."

Scanning the figures and doing some sort of elementary arithmetic, one came to the conclusion that net output per man-shift had increased some 230 percent in just two decades, and open-cut coal mining had increased about 300 percent during the same time span.

Now, one could consider this "the wave of the future." With no significant increase in population, and with coal mine employment cut nearly in half during the twenty-year span, the Australians had found the secret of the 21st Century; let the machines do the work; that's what they were invented for.

As one read the statistics, this was, for coal, only the beginning of the beginning.

Associated Australian Oil Fields announced in June 1971 that measured, indicated and inferred coal reserves in situ to a depth of 1000 feet below the surface of Hail Creek, eighty miles southwest of Mackay, Queensland, were more than 750 million tons.
—"Quarterly Review," *Australian Mineral Industry*, Vol. 24, September, 1971

Nor was this by any means all. Someplace down there was a future fire-breathing, smoke belching dragon, coiled for the centuries:

The world's largest deposits of brown coal are in Victoria —an estimated 20,000,000,000 tons in Latrobe Valley alone—there are four other Victorian deposits.
— *The Pacific Book of Australiana*, Angus and Robertson, Sydney, 1967

Considering its importance, it was not easy to find much about coal to laugh at, but an entry in the Australian fact book caused a minor chuckle. The entry says, "The open-cut brown coal mine at Yallourn, Victoria is claimed to be the largest man-made hole in the world—so big that the whole of Melbourne could be put in it."

Some dedicated "Sydneysiders" might wish that this would be done.

Brown coal was not the only enormous store of fuel for the future. According to the *National Development Quarterly* (June, 1972) "The Bureau of Mineral Resources of the Department of National Development assessed black coal reserves no deeper than 2,000 feet at nearly 24,000 million tons . . . Total recoverable reserves of coking quality coal amounted to 7,600 million tons . . . It is expected that continued exploration, particularly in Queensland, will increase overall reserves of black coal.

"In recent years, production of black coal for export, particularly coking coals for Japanese steel mills, has grown into a major industry for New South Wales and Queensland, but even without this trade, coal mining would be of major importance to the community. This is because of the steadily rising demand for electricity, generated for the most part in coal-burning thermal stations, and because of the rising demand from the Australian steel industry."

It was not until 1915, at that same famed coal port of Newcastle, did Australia produce its first steel from an integrated iron and steel works. It was a good time for it; World War I had begun and there was a suddenly created world market.

Since then, steel making capacity had been constantly increasing; giving, along with greatly increased Australian thermal-power needs, a major twin market for the thousands of millions of tons of already discovered Australian coal.

Not even the Raft's officers knew how much more might be hidden in bunkers yet to be found.

Moonie Queensland 1961

It was there all the time; several million years of it. But nobody saw it; its guiding light had not been lit yet.

But it was there, the oil and gas to power the Stone Raft on its voyage through time. It had been first discovered around the turn of the century, but not in commercial quantities, and anyway, in the Australian economy of that time there was little need for it.

World War II changed all that. The Moonie field was discovered in 1961; then things began to happen quite fast:

Another field was discovered at Barrow Island, off the north coast of Western Australia, in 1964. Offshore drilling on the Gippsland Shelf of Bass Strait began off Sale in 1965 and subsequently revealed large reserves of oil and natural gas. Gas fields have been discovered also in Queensland, South Australia, Western Australia and the Northern Territory . . .
—Mineral Deposits, Geographic Section, Department of National Development, Canberra, 1970

None of these deposits were very big, and under the pressures of technological society were not going to last very long. But at least they were there, and the expectancy was that other fields and reserves would be discovered. If so, this would be important to Australia's future, until new forms of energy could be found and developed. This was true of other countries as well, but for Australia the problem was specially crucial because of its relative isolation from large oil producing countries.

Thus the joy of success in finding commercially worth-while quantities of crude oil after many years of search and the expenditure of more than $750 million by private and government organizations on exploration is now tempered by a realization it needs to be continued unabated.
Australia needs to find about 1,000 million barrels of crude oil every two years to maintain even a 70 percent self-sufficiency.
—National Development Quarterly, March, 1971

Because so little real exploration had been done, and because the continent was so large, it seemed likely that there would be major discoveries and development of oil and gas reserves well before the year 2000.

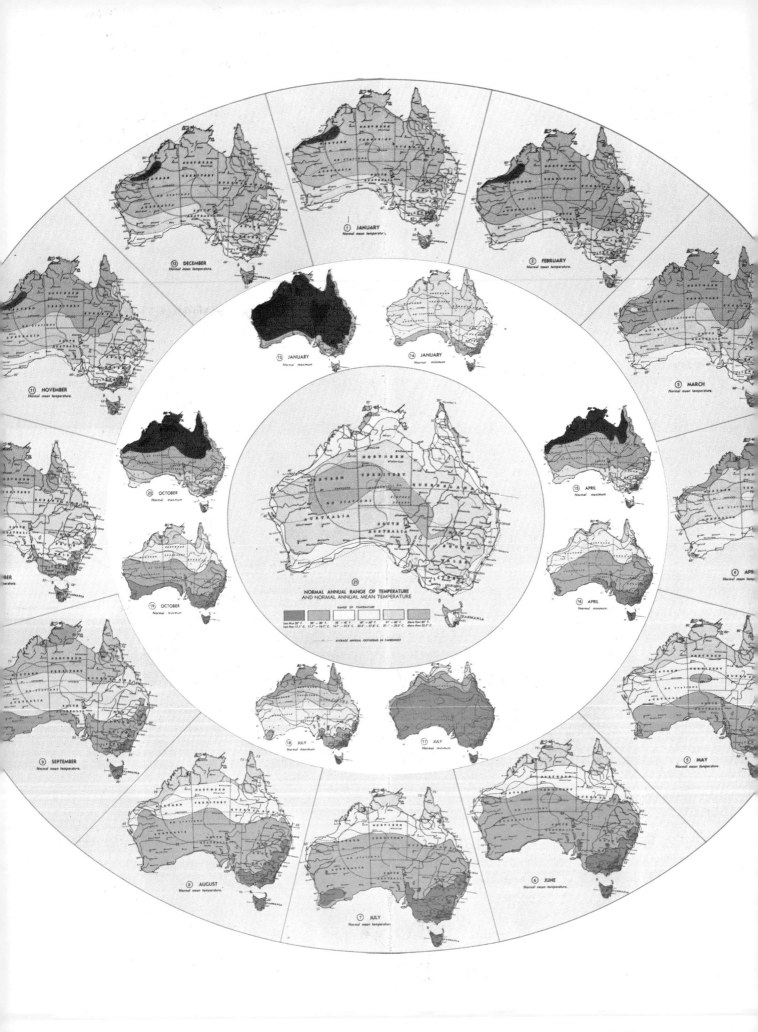

12 DECEMBER
Normal mean temperature.

1 JANUARY
Normal mean temperature.

2 FEBRUARY
Normal mean temperature.

3 MARCH
Normal mean temperature.

11 NOVEMBER
Normal mean temperature.

13 JANUARY
Normal maximum

14 JANUARY
Normal minimum

20 OCTOBER
Normal maximum

15 APRIL
Normal maximum

19 OCTOBER
Normal minimum

16 APRIL
Normal minimum

4 APRIL
Normal mean temperature.

21 NORMAL ANNUAL RANGE OF TEMPERATURE
AND NORMAL ANNUAL MEAN TEMPERATURE

RANGE OF TEMPERATURE

AVERAGE ANNUAL ISOTHERMS IN FAHRENHEIT

9 SEPTEMBER
Normal mean temperature.

18 JULY
Normal maximum

17 JULY
Normal minimum

5 MAY
Normal mean temperature.

8 AUGUST
Normal mean temperature.

7 JULY
Normal mean temperature.

6 JUNE
Normal mean temperature.

In the middle of all sits Sun enthroned. In this most beautiful temple, could we place this luminary in any other position from which we can illuminate the whole at once? He is rightly called the Lamp, the Mind, the Ruler of the Universe . . . So the Sun sits as upon a royal throne, ruling his children the planets which encircle him . . . Meanwhile the Earth conceives by the Sun and becomes pregnant with an annual birth.

Nicolaus Copernicus
De Revolutionibus Orbium Caelestium Frauenberg
1543

Everywhere, Australia: Date ∞

Even though the coal in the bunkers was busting at the seams, on a long trip it would eventually run out. If the raft were to continue its Odyssey through space and time, it would need some power source to supplement, and ultimately replace, the coal in the bunkers and the oil in the tanks.

As a gifted poet named Rupert Brooke once said, "If anything can help him now, the kind old sun will know." Squinting over the yardarm, one could see that if there was one thing Australia had in abundance, the kind old sun was it. The thousands of square miles of sun-baked arid and semi-arid deck could provide, through the use of solar energy, all the power the old raft would ever need.

The raft bobbed slowly through the seas of time bathed in the radiance of its closest star. To one's bare feet, the stone plates of the deck were almost unbearably hot—hot as the steel mesh gratings of the coal and oil-fired engine room walkways.

Australia's dead heart may one day become a giant power house supporting a big industrial complex. The burning, empty desert could be transformed into flourishing communities, self-sufficient in food and water, and living in air-conditioned, pollution free comfort. This could be a picture of our outback by the turn of the century if more emphasis is placed on research into the harnessing of solar energy. Mr. W. W. S. Charters, senior lecturer in mechanical engineering at Melbourne University, foresees the time when acres of solar cells—similar to those on spacecraft—will directly convert the sun's radiation in our outback into electricity.
—*The Herald*, January 4, 1972.

Surely something could be done with all this free star-born energy. But how? Well, there are many ways, but making them work was something else. The fact that something was abundant and "free" does not necessarily mean that one could use it. The largesse of radiant energy poured down like a rain of golden coins. But devising a net to catch them, or a safe to store them in against a rainy day, was not as easy as it looked.

Australia is a land of superlatives. It is generally considered the oldest (perhaps the first) land mass, remotest (from Western civilization), lowest (only 6 per cent of its land is more than 2,000 feet above sea level), driest (more than half the land is desert), emptiest (nearly three-fourths of the continent is virtually uninhabited), and smallest of the populated continents.
It is the only continent that is also a country—and the only country founded without internal wars or revolution . . .
—AUSTRALIA: THE FORGING OF A NATION, Field Enterprises Educational Corporation, 1970.

The most obvious and simplest way to catch the sunbeams would be to build roof and exposed wall areas with glass bonded to a highly conductive, black-surfaced metal as the underlayer and attached to that, pipes or conduits that circulated the water heated by the trapped solar rays. The sun warms the water sufficiently for washing, shaving and maintaining warmth during the night hours. The heat also possibly could be used to produce air conditioning during the day along the same principles of gas-fired refrigerators that, paradoxically, turn heat into cold.

While such a system of black plates would not actually *produce* power, it could greatly reduce the necessity for using natural gas, fuel oil, coal or electrical power for much of the year in most of Australia. No costly electrical transmission lines would be needed, nor pipelines either, but some sort of conventional "standby" heat source would be needed for use during prolonged periods of rain or heavy overcast. Even so, the overall cost of space and water temperature control would be less than present systems, and would have the added advantage that the use of solar heat would not pollute the atmosphere, involve ecological damage (as coal mining and oil drilling do) and there would be no waste disposal problem (such as that from nuclear power producing plants).

Some such solar-heated houses, as well as simple rooftop solar-heated water tanks had been built and worked in those parts of the United States (Florida and the Southwest) whose climate was much like most of Australia's and even performed well in areas as far north as Maine and Washington, D.C.

The major problem was the cost of components, since most of them had to be custom made. Under mass production, they might not cost more than traditional building materials. Even though the solar energy construction would cost more to begin with, it would be a one-time cost; probably much lower over a period of time than the cost of constantly buying coal, gas, oil or electricity. There would be no working parts to wear out and, properly designed, no maintenance nor service costs.

For Australia, such a system could lead to a large secondary industry to fabricate, market and install the relatively unsophisticated components. Roof and sunny-side wall panels of glass, metal and water conduits could come off assembly lines as easily as plywood or wallboard does now, in standard sizes and with leak-proof,

interlocking edges or metal or plastic. Silica for the glass could be a by-product of alumina processing and of rutile (beach sand containing a commercially profitable amount of titanium dioxide) mining. Or it might be possible to skip glass altogether and just use sheet metal sprayed with some sort of plastic that would serve the same function as glass; namely, to allow the solar rays to be absorbed by the black metal underneath, and by trapping the heat so that it did not simply irradiate off into space again. Circulating conduits could be attached to the underside of the metal plate by now existing adhesives, and the pipes could be made of light metals or plastics.

(One thought there might be some way to adapt the many corrugated roofs of the older buildings throughout Australia, so that the depressions in the corrugations could serve as conduits for sheets of water, running under a superimposed plate of glass and black metal. Where water was scarce, the same water could be recirculated throughout the system in the same way that water in garden or park fountains is recirculated. A minimal amount of electrical energy would be needed, and in a closed system, there should be only a tiny evaporation loss.)

A pipe dream? No. The techniques for the direct use of solar energy for space and water heating had already been developed and used in Europe and North America. All that really was needed was to put the systems together for Australia, which was, sun-speaking, best endowed of all.

Once one captured them, how could the sunbeams be stored? One way could be to pass the hot water from the roof and wall solar collectors into a water tank surrounded by rocks in the basement. The rocks would absorb the incoming heat during the daylight hours, and radiate it back during the dark hours of the night. A fan could be used to circulate the warm air through ducts into living quarters upstairs. Since warm air rises naturally, a fan might not even be needed. Such systems had been tried and appeared to work, even in such unlikely places as Washington, D. C., where winter weather is even colder and more overcast than that in Melbourne.

Another way to store the heat for a dark night or a rainy or overcast day could be to store the heat in "eutectic" salts. These salts melt as they absorb heat and then solidify again when the temperature drops, and give off heat in the process. It was a sort of "recycling" of energy. The salts could be put in used one- or five-gallon petrol cans, and built into walls where the solar-heated air or water melted them, and then during the night, would gradually release the heat.

However, since the old stone raft of Australia was carrying a lot of rocks as ballast, it could be cheaper just to line the basement area with them.

The whole system of collecting solar energy in the form of heat to relieve the pressure on more traditional systems seemed like something worth looking into. Particularly in a country where sunshine was abundant, that had all the basic building materials in profusion, that needed light manufacturing industries to keep up the level of employment, and dispersion of job opportunities and tax bases away from densely populated areas, and a continent and culture that was partially dependent on costly imported petroleum, long pipelines, and electrical transmission systems.

Of course, none of this rigamarole would *produce* energy (energy cannot be produced, anyway—it can only be transformed to suit man's needs. The heat from a burning log in the fireplace was stored there as radiant energy from the sun many a long year ago; just as it was in coal and petroleum). This also appeared to be true of hydroelectric power; the radiance from the sun pulled the water up to form into clouds that eventually precipitated rain that filled the lakes behind the dams. The artificial, man-made waterfalls turned the turbines that transformed the solar energy into electrical currents. At least, theoretically, assuming the planet Earth spun off from the sun, even nuclear energy was derived, billions of years ago, from that grand and smiling, radiant old man.

Australia is, in general, a land of warmth and sunshine. Uncomfortable temperature and humidity conditions are experienced for only a few months of the year excepting the far north. Rainfall is not over-abundant, and the development of natural resources has called for virility and resourcefulness in the rural population. Earlier generations of settlers have faced droughts, floods, storms and other visitations which have caused loss and damage. The effects in recent times of such happenings have been largely minimized by efficient warning systems in the case of storms and floods and by hand-feeding and removal of stock in the case of drought, by orchard or vineyard heating in the case of frosts, and by the organization of very efficient fire-fighting organizations to combat bush and grass fires. Large areas of semi-arid land have been brought under profitable cultivation by irrigation . . .
—CLIMATIC REGIONS, Department of National Development, Canberra, 1954.

Electrical power *could* be transformed from solar radiation. Suppose one went out on the sun-bright deck, carrying lens from the craft's searchlights. Jury-rig some sort of stands for them out of scrap tubing from the engine room and mount the slowly rotating stand (powered by a geared-down washing machine engine) so that the mirrors would always face the sun and focus the reflected rays on the same spot. Put a can filled with water there at the focal point. Presto! Instant steam. Which, if one wanted to continue the primitive system of heating water to create steam to drive a turbine, to turn a shaft, to turn coils of wire cutting through a magnetic field, one could convert solar energy into electrical energy in a form that would be useful to the crew.

Such devices of mirrors had been built previously in other countries and they could convert sunshine into concentrated heat to as high a magnitude as 5000°F. And these simple mechanisms had worked in places much less sun-filled than most of Australia. Most conventional power plants based on the steam/turbine system operate at temperatures of about 1000°F. Sun-power is ahead by five lengths, in the comparison of the two systems.

Using focussed mirrors to concentrate solar radiation on a point receptor is quite literally "getting something for nothing." It does have the disability that converting sunlight into steam, to drive turbines, is an extraordinary way to transform energy into its electrical form.

Even so, it looked like a more efficient way than using fossil fuels—coal, gas and oil to perform the same job. By-products of the solar-mirror system could be used to melt refractory metals (this had been done in Europe for years) and in the process, extract the heat given off by the cooling melts to produce steam, thus finally arriving at both material products and a source for electrical energy at the same time.

Any Boy Scout or Boy Ranger knew that one could start a fire in seconds, given the sun, a magnifying glass and some combustible material. (On a much larger scale, this was said to have been done by Archimedes in 212 B.C., who used huge metallic mirrors to focus the sun's rays and cause the sails of the Roman fleet attacking Syracuse to burst into flame.)

In an only slightly more sophisticated way, it had been suggested that—in the

Australian Scientists Study Solar Energy

Catching Sunbeams
Old Dream of Putting Sun's Power to Work Gets Renewed Attention

Earthly Energy Shortages Spur Research Into Ways To Collect, Use Solar Rays

Satellites & Eutectic Salts

closing part of the Twentieth Century—it should be possible to put giant lenses in permanent orbit, focussing the sun's rays on selected spots on the earth's surface cutting through clouds and fog; the heat thus generated to be transformed into electrical power. It might have sounded

> But within the broad bounds indicated by the physical environment the particular patterns of land use are largely influenced by the social environment, which includes such broad elements as the historical background of the community, the present state of technology, and the nature of the economic system. In newly settled countries such as Australia, where land use has from early days been geared largely to the requirements of the local and overseas urban markets, economic considerations have formed the primary element in the social environment. It is largely as a result of the interplay of physical and economic considerations that the present pattern of dominant land use has been evolved.
> —DOMINANT LAND USE, by A. J. ROSE, Senior Lecturer in Geography, Canberra University College, Department of National Development, Canberra, A.C.T., (pg. 2).

like science fiction, but the theoretical basis already existed and the technological capability was shambling along close behind.

There seemed to be no reason why Australia, in cooperation with countries that already had a highly advanced space technology, should not lead the way. Australia had the technical resources, the sunlight and land areas that would be far enough from populated areas to be safe (just in case the early attempts went wrong). It would take a lot of capital investment—but what doesn't?

Okay, standing there, daydreaming of an eye in the sky which could be only pie in the sky, one could consider the possible, even probable, applications of space technology originally developed by the

Russians and the Americans, for exotic means of converting solar rays into man-useful energy.

Consider the photovoltaic. These little man-made creatures are thin wafers of silicon, that like diamonds in the sky, have the ability to transform solar radiation directly into electrical current. They were developed to power the electronic equipment aboard spacecraft, so that the powered umbilical cord to Mother Earth could be severed.

These little solar-energy-transforming wafers were not much in demand and were difficult to produce. So despite the fact that silica is one of the most abundant materials on earth (silicon is the basic element, coupled with oxygen and certain impurities) the little things were terribly expensive to produce.

Still, there was something promising here for the conversion of radiant energy directly into electricity. One of the crew had been puttering around with a solar cell made from cadmium sulfide on thin sheets of plastic. These, if the scheme worked out, could be mass produced at a much lower unit price than the silicon coins of the sun.

> Australia is the driest of all the continents. About one-third is desert, and a good deal of the remainder has very little effective rainfall. More than half the continent receives, on average, less than 15 inches of rain a year, and even over much of the higher rainfall country, falls tend to be markedly seasonal, or erratic, or both. Largely as a result of these unfavourable rainfall conditions, water resources over most of the continent are meagre. Flow in the majority of streams is very variable, with long periods of low or no flow interspersed with floods at irregular intervals. Most of the important rivers flow from the limited areas of higher land near the eastern coast.
> —CONSERVATION OF SURFACE WATER, Department of National Development, Canberra, A.C.T., 1956.

At any rate, suppose the solar cells instantly converted radiant energy into usable electrical current? One didn't really need too much electrical current during the daylight hours, except perhaps for air conditioning. There were storage batteries that could siphon off the unused energy during the day, hold it, and release it as needed at night, then recharge themselves the next day. Perhaps some storage batteries could be invented, developed and produced that could operate for longer periods when the sky was overcast and the little wafers on the roof were taking holiday. Perhaps some might be developed that could convert other solar-originated wavelengths, that cut through clouds, into useful energy.

The batteries or storage cells would be much like water reservoirs that held the runoff from the rains or melting snows, and very much like the rocks in the basement in a less sophisticated system—take the energy in by day, release it at night.

Now for the moment, suppose such a system could be developed; then the world one lived in could change dramatically. Most every building could be roofed with wafers, and generate all the electrical energy needed. There would be no more generating plants (what happens to the coal industry?), no more elaborate transmission networks (where did all those people go?), no more public utilities with their vast bureaucracies mostly engaged in sending out bills (what papers were they shuffling now?). There also would be no smoke belching from generating station smokestacks (but if a smokestack cannot belch, what is it supposed to do?). A different world.

Linked to computers, such a system could transmit periodicals, whole books, medical suggestions for home treatment until the doctor arrives by helicopter, 3-D "how to do it" information for home improvements; political, economic, and educational information. With techniques already developed, facsimiles of desired information or entertainment could be stored on video tape cartridges 24 hours a day, and with a proper retrieval system, read or watched or listened to at any convenient time. Gone are the days when one had to get up early in the morning, bathe,

---

The situation of Australia is . . . comparable to that of the southern States of the U.S.A. and Mexico, or northern Africa, including the Sahara Desert and the Mediterranean Sea, or China and Japan, including Indo-China. That the pattern of climate in Australia differs in many respects from those of the countries in corresponding latitudes in the northern hemisphere is attributable to the dominating influences of the land masses in the northern hemisphere on the air masses which traverse these regions. Although lying in the anti-cyclonic belt in which the main desert regions of the world are found, the oceanic influences of the southern hemisphere modify to some degree the extremes to which the continents of Africa, Asia and America are subject.
—J. C. FOLEY, Chief Scientific Officer; Meteorological Branch, Department of the Interior, *Climatic Regions,* Department of National Development, Canberra, 1954.

---

shave, drive a car or take public transport, in order to answer a telephone.

Now it appeared that any country could achieve this system at any time, but there were few, if any, technologically advanced countries in the world that had the space, the time, and the available solar energy as Australia did, to make the silicon wafer on the roof beat his wings in the soft supersuration of cosmic power.

In just three decades? Why not? Everything crouched in readiness. The 21st Century was scattered all over the place, just waiting to be born. Technological conception was already a reality.

It was only a matter of time.

Looking down on the big deck, and squinting a little, one could see a thin red line; the Australian Overland Telegraph. It is considered to be at least the equivalent of the Transatlantic Cable, but longer—4,500 miles from Java to Port Darwin on the North Coast, and overland south to Alice Springs to connect with existing telegraph lines through Adelaide to Melbourne and Sydney on the Southeast Coast. The project was completed in 1872. What follows are excerpts from Ernestine Hill's incomparable account of the saga. It shows at least two things: the almost unbelievable courage of the Australian people and that this is a continent like no other on earth.
—ERNESTINE HILL: *The Territory*, Angus and Robertson, Ltd., Sydney, 1951

THE SINGING STRING

An afternoon's 'motor-run now from Elsey Station are the famous Red Lily Lagoons—Yaalput—a close weave of scarlet for three square miles, the glory of the Roper. In New Year '72 was written their greatest page of history. Three of the telegraph parties were marooned there, within fifty miles of each other without knowing, living on flour and the last of the bully beef, when into that world of waters came Ralph Milner, first drover from south to north, with four thousand sheep.

His story begins at Killapaninna on the Cooper, fifteen hundred miles south, a station long abandoned on the shores of Lake Eyre, its fences now buried and its lofty old rooms filled to the ceilings with sand. In 1870 Ralph Milner owned the station and his wife died there. He built a cairn to her memory in the wild-flower sandhills. When the Government offered £10,000 reward for the opening of the stock route from Adelaide to Darwin with sheep or cattle for the Telegraph parties, Milner set out, with his brother John and seven men, droving seven thousand sheep and three hundred horses. The Government changed when he was half-way across, and he never collected the money. His men, like Stuart's and Todd's, were paid 25s. a week. They carried a year's stores on bullock drays, with greyhounds and sheep-dogs to guard the flock, also a black-boy and his lubra, faithful Charley and Fannie, every night for eighteen months building little brush yards.

From Peake Station in a cruel summer they whipped on the sheep till they were blind under the sulphur sky and crippled from the stones. One stage was eighty miles with no water. On Christmas Day 1870 they stopped at a mudspring to wash clothes, clean firearms and shift the loading. They found some bags of sago soaked through with kerosene, but dared not throw them away. That sago was their Christmas dinner, 1871.

The Finke was a river of sand, its pools all salt, but they dug soaks, and one night the river came down from rains in the ranges. It was two fathoms deep for a hundred miles by morning. They were trapped for a month, horses bogged and wagons floating. Wild dogs circled with melancholy howling.

When the Finke had subsided to a quarter of a mile, they made it a swim—the first hundred sheep went down to their bellies in quicksand. The men worked the water out of the sand and saved them. A stiff current carried the next lot downstream—all hands and horses swimming. At last they built a bridge, of spinifex and gum-

boughs, five hundred yards long, over the quicksands and the flowing channels and, with a few goats to lead them, seven thousand sheep scrambled across in single file.

Out of the bogs, the next trial was a plague of rats. The men fought them, in moving blur of thousands, to save the flour. Thankfully they rested at the lonely Telegraph camp of Alice Springs, and went on—to a valley of fatal beauty. Beyond the Devil's Marbles the gastrolobium was in blossom, tall as English hollyhocks and softly bright as wallflowers. On a blithe morning the drovers were wearing it in their hats . . . two thousand sheep were dead that night, the pain-maddened bullocks tossing the carcasses on their horns. Gastrolobium is swift and deadly poison to stock—many a mob of cattle has since perished at that spot.

Tragedy caught up with them at Attack Creek. Blacks were mustering for mischief—smokes all round. John Milner unwisely made friends with the natives and brought them in to camp. He was waddied to death while he lay sleeping in the shade, his grave the first of many on the overland track.

By the moon, the mopoke and the dingo's howl, each night the shepherds camped a few miles northward. There was trouble with the blacks all the way, but the dogs were their defenders. One morning they "found a black-fellow with his throat torn out, and many tracks of blood." Grim years, the seventies, in the outback of Australia.

At Newcastle Waters, through dense walls of lancewood, they chopped a passage for the sheep, a long seven miles—you will still find it on the Stuart Highway, known as Milner's Cutting. So they came to the Roper when it was six miles wide—it rained inches every day for the next three months. They still had four thousand sheep, herded on a ridge south of Red Lily, paddocked in

natural walls of grass. When the sun came out for an hour they killed sheep and ate them, and bagged the mutton chips—you cannot jerk meat in the rain. Flour, tea and salt were done, they lived on sheep and cold water. The bullocks were bogged miles back, with most of the packs and swags, horses drowned and running wild. They boiled the kerosene sago for a treat on Christmas Day.

By February the plains were an inland sea with breaking waves, crocodiles swimming in the lagoons like sharks in the Indian Ocean. In March the unmerciful rain stopped. Rutt's, MacLachlan's and Burton's parties were a surprise to each other, all starving on flour while Milner's were starving on mutton a day's ride away. They boated over the sheep in an upturned cart, eleven at a time, and that night Todd's Men had chops for tea.

Between King River and Bitter Springs is Providence Knoll, a pretty spinney of pines and jungle where Rutt and his men raced for safety when their drays were under water on the flat. There they lived for six weeks on ship's biscuit, the skeleton horses drowning their heads in flood waters, trying to crop the vivid green grass below. Near by is All Saints' Well, named by Ringwood, which had saved their lives a few months before in the scorched and unbearable dry. Some years ago at Epping, Sydney, I met David Melville, a white-headed patriarch of ninety-five years, who was with Rutt at Providence Knoll and helped to count Milner's sheep. He told me that when hopes were lowest and tempers worst in the accursed rain, he made four sets of playing cards out of bully beef tins, painting them in spades, clubs and hearts. The men played euchre in the dripping bush, good-humouredly trumping each others' tricks till the floods went down.

When the Roper was a river again in a thousand miles of glue, W. G. Stretton, Burton's store-

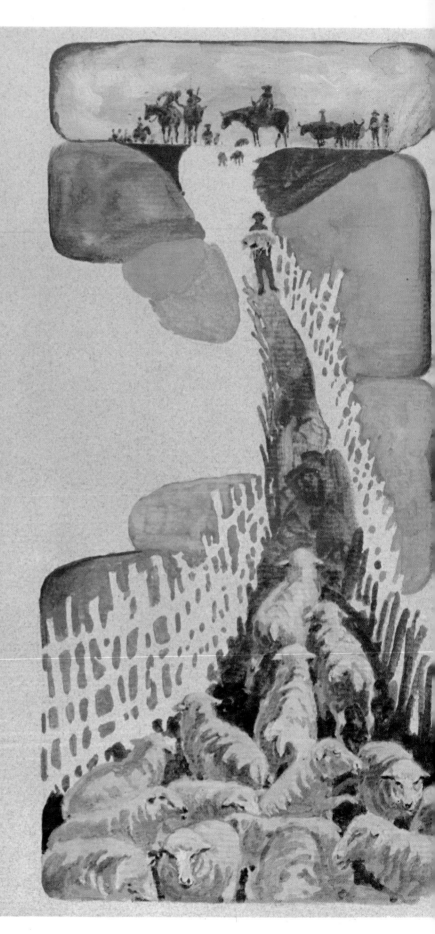

keeper, with eight others, floated in the body of a dray to Roper Bar, and pulled back two hundred miles against the stiff current, bringing the glad news that Todd's ships were in the river, Todd and Patterson on the way up with a hundred and fifty packhorses bringing food and clothing for the camps.

There was a "toff's party" at Red Lily—a razor, a shirt and trousers, a silver-mounted pipe to every man, Milner's roast mutton, a plum duff and a nobbler of whisky to toast the Overland Telegraph Line. It was disastrously late, but so far the B.A.T. had taken no action. The heroes had not suffered in vain. They still might cover the ground in time.

Skies cleared—the wire raced on. From twenty poles to the mile Todd reduced the number to sixteen, to ten. By May, twelve hundred miles were completed from Port Augusta to Tennant's Creek, and three hundred miles from Darwin south to Birdum Creek, named by Patterson for his wife, a Miss Birdum. Three hundred miles to go—the end in sight.

All the world was impatient to hear the first message through. Todd had an inspiration—he would run an *estafette* with four relays of horses, field operators with the construction parties to spell out messages in Morse at each end of the Line.

On 26th June the packhorses of Ray Parkin Boucaut galloped three hundred miles south from Katherine with souvenir cables and the first international newsflash to Australia—that, over the Alabama question, England and the United States were about to declare war. News of the Franco-Prussian War, less than a week old, at Australia's breakfast table was a marvel of the age.

The thrill was brief. Next day the machines were silent. The cable had broken in deep water off the Java shore.

As was true on all long voyages there was a lot of livestock aboard. One could muster a lively mob, gamboling on the foredeck. The kangaroo bounced, the wallaby jumped, the koala clung to an ancient dream, the cattle moaned, the pigs grunted, the wombat snuffled his weary way down the corridors of time, and the magpies quarreled with the galahs. But the sheep were in the meadow and all was right with the world.

No one was likely to sit around on his out-back waiting for the professors to tell him thirty years later what he should do. The Australians were not made that way. They would give her a go and improvise and some of their schemes might even work. Some might not. But given the vigor of the Australian cricketer, they would most likely make more runs than they lost.

What things might one try until the Canberra technicians and Australian National University and the CSIRO and the Department of Minerals and Energy told them what they had done wrong?

Lots of quite practical things can be done at relatively low cost.

When and if it ever rains, most of the water runs off through the usually dry river courses and ends up in the ocean. One simple way to counteract this is to harrow the stream beds. This could be done by flying in grading equipment by heavy-duty helicopters for a few hours, then fly the equipment to another site and do the same thing.

The result could be transverse ridges and hollows, much like waves in the sea, that would slow down the runoff and hopefully trap some of the water to sink underground, away from evaporation and ultimately to raise local water tables for easier pumping, and a longer reserve during the dry seasons.

This would assume the availability of grading equipment and suitably large helicopters. If we had some eggs, we could have a ham and egg sandwich, if we had some ham.

So maybe, for Australia, that might not work, or at least for a long time. Think of something else.

Why not "wild farming"? The native plants and animals have learned over tens of thousands of years to survive the brackish water, the frequent scarcity of any water at all for long periods of time, and the torrential downpours of "The Wet." As native plants and animals, they have as high a food content (for humans) as any of their imported domestic equivalents. The native species did not require man-made watering, nor fencing; naturally reproduced themselves in balance with environmental changes, and did not damage the ecology, as did the sheep.

Moreover, they—the indigenous animals —could roam the same range as the sheep and cattle, because they ate different parts of the same native plants.

The hides of the kangaroo and wallabies sold for much more on the international market than the meat, wool and hides of sheep did. There was the problem of salmonella in the kangaroo, but this could be eliminated over a period of time, just as it had largely been eliminated with American cattle.

The problem of the 'roos went much

deeper than that. The animals themselves were unique in the world and thus were an important tourist attraction. (One could walk around and pet them in the zoos at Brisbane, Melbourne and Sydney. One seldom saw them in the wild, except perhaps early in the morning on the Ghan train speeding its 1098-mile trip from Alice Springs to Adelaide. Or in the twilight, on the road through the national reserve above Canberra, from a car.)

... our mammals are singularly unco-operative. The great majority are small, as we think of size in wild animals, and are nocturnal and cryptic in their habits ... the red and grey kangaroos provide a refreshing exception because their size makes them easily seen and observed, and because they are often about and active well before darkness falls and after the dawn has broken ...
—FRANCIS RATCLIFFE: "The Commercial Hunting of Kangaroos," *Occasional Publication No. 4,* Australian Conservation Foundation, Melbourne, July, 1970

Whether by dawn or twilight, or midnight spotlight, the array always seemed to be nearly the same: the big male standing erect on sentinel duty while the does and joeys (baby kangaroos) were asleep, or at least lying down in a semicircle around him. A sight to remember, for it might soon be gone forever.

One could not help but wonder what might be done in the next thirty years to preserve the species.

The provision of a suitable place to live is generally more important to an animal's survival than protective legislation. The sheep country of New South Wales once supported a fairly abundant population of small kangaroo like animals ... These creatures were never persecuted by hunting, but disappeared nonetheless when the sheep and the white man altered the environment.
—"The Red Kangaroo," *Rural Research* (CSIRO), March, 1965

A parliamentary committee to study the conservation and commercial exploitation of kangaroos issued an interim report (November, 1971) in which it said that while most of the larger species of kangaroo are

not in danger of extinction from commercial harvesting, drought or destruction of habitat, a number of smaller species are, though not necessarily from commercial exploitation:

The endangered species listed include the following small kangaroos and wallabies: brush-tailed rat kangaroo; lesueur's rat-kangaroo, desert or plain rat-kangaroo, long-nosed rat-kangaroo, musky rat-kangaroo, western hare-wallaby, ring-tailed rock wallaby, bridled nail-tailed wallaby, crescent nail-tailed wallaby; and the white-throated or parma wallaby.
—IAN BISSET: "The Future of the Kangaroo," *The Canberra Times,* January 6, 1972

None of these species is of any particular commercial value, so their danger is not from the hunters but from changes in their habitat brought about by agricultural, timber and mining practices. Perhaps in the cosmos, the survival of these silly little creatures, who have never met a payroll, paid union dues, voted for Prime Minister, is of no consequence. Yet these little people constitute a gene pool of animals unique in the world; once gone, there is no way to bring them back again. And man, for all his omnipotence, does not know to what end these creatures were created, nor what role in the future of the planet they might be intended to play. There should be some way to pursue man's game and still preserve the creatures on the sidelines. Mankind may need someone to cheer him on in the late innings.

It seemed that some more research should be done; and quickly, before the graziers and fast-buck poachers extermi-nate both the big kangaroos and the smaller ones. Some research *had* been done.

Scientists have now accumulated sufficient information on the biology of the red kangaroo and its interaction with vegetation and grazing livestock to allow a scien-tifically based programme of commercial use, control and conservation to be formulated in general system of management.
—"Learning to Live with Kangaroos," *Rural Research CSIRO*, June, 1969

One would start with at least two main considerations. One of these would be that the kangaroos tend to stay in the same general area of about ten square miles, but are nomadic during times of drought (some tagged reds have travelled 120 miles or more in search of food and water). So population density may vary enormously in different localities during the dry years and the concentration of kangaroos may seriously compete for food and water with domestic livestock, who would already be having trouble enough to stay alive. In the dry years, this could create serious prob-lems of density and migratory control; problems yet to be solved.

The question of movement is relevant to both conserva-tion and control of the species. Periodic influxes of mobs from great distances could make a mockery of some types of control. Conversely, conservation must be based on provision of living areas sufficiently large to cope with the normal movements that the species employ for survival.
—"Learning to Live With Kangaroos," *Rural Research CSIRO*, June, 1969

Report calls for tighter controls on 'roo killing

From MICHELLE GRATTAN

CANBERRA. — A Federal parliamentary committee has recommended setting aside large areas of land as national parks and reserves for kangaroos and other native fauna.

Civilisation: the message of doom for the kangaroo

Marsupials *versus* livestock

The introduction of sheep and cattle has been advantageous to the euro and red kangaroo, but many species of small marsupial are either extinct or in great danger of becoming so.

Another consideration was that different species of kangaroos eat differently, so that it should be possible to raise several species on the same land with domestic livestock, without causing serious ecologic damage.

... it has become clear that there is little overlap between the areas that the main kangaroo species occupy. They differ in the food and/or the type of terrain and shelter preferred. If species overlap, as do red and grey kangaroos in parts of southwestern Queensland where they sometimes share the same paddocks and shelter in the same scrub, the species remain isolated ecologically by their food preferences ...

An important implication of differing food preferences among kangaroo species, and between them and sheep, is that management and conservation procedures must be aimed at a particular kangaroo.

—"Learning to Live With Kangaroos," *Rural Research CSIRO*, June, 1969

What seemed to be a contradiction from a conservationist's point of view is that the introduction of sheep on grazing lands by the European settlers may actually have increased the total population of the larger species of kangaroos in some areas. Sheep troughs sited every few miles provided more convenient sources of water for the kangaroos and the sheep grazing kept the vegetation cut low, providing the fresh green shoots favored by the kangaroos over the ungrazed, taller and drier natural vegetation.

Shaffert had been born too late. The mail coach was going out of fashion as he grew up, and he had to find stockman's work instead.

There is one story he still tells about Joe Hirschberg, when he drove alongside a somewhat unusual passenger for those parts. The man was a commercial traveller and new to the outback. As they raced on through the bush towards Croydon, he asked if they would see any kangaroos.

"Don't tell me you've never seen one?" Hirschberg asked him. "There's hundreds along these roads."

After a moment's reflection, he added:

"I tell you what, friend. There's one big old grey we'll meet this side of Croydon. Real character, that fellow. Every time I come along, he stands beside the road to collect his mail."

"You're joking."

"It's the sober truth, friend. We'll see him in the next couple of miles."

Sure enough, out of the heat haze of that late afternoon, they saw a grey kangaroo bounding towards the road. As soon as it heard the coach, it propped. It stood there completely still. Hirschberg waited his time, then suddenly stood up and yelled. "No mail for you today!" He cracked his mighty whip. The roo turned to bound away into the scrub.

"Well!" said the amazed traveller. "I'd never have believed it. Not if I hadn't seen him with my own eyes."

GHOST TOWNS OF AUSTRALIA
ROLLCALL FOR PIONEERS
—GEORGE FARWELL, Rigby Ltd., Adelaide, 1965

'Roos being wiped out

Kangaroos in danger find a new home

117

In many parts of the country, though, the advent of roads and fences had reduced the kangaroo population to virtually nil, as did the spread of suburban communities in the coastal areas. Like all other man-tampering with nature, whatever he did was a mixed blessing and created most complex problems to try to solve.

Then there was the question whether, on the same rangeland, the kangaroo competed with sheep and cattle for the same food. Most graziers felt that the kangaroos competed for the available food and water and thus reduced the farmers' chances to raise more domestic livestock; and the kangaroo, in their eyes, thus became a pest.

Such information as is available suggests that although kangaroos and sheep tend to eat the same classes of plants, they often prefer different species and in different proportions. Thus, they seldom compete directly, especially when food is readily available. Red kangaroos need a higher protein diet than sheep and cattle and cannot utilize fibre and roughage as readily as the ruminants. In general, the kangaroo prefers short green growth and leaves long growth, both green and dry, to the livestock. This has been observed in all study areas—including central Australia, southwestern Queensland, western New South Wales, and the Riverina—and for both sheep and cattle.
— "Learning to Live With Kangaroos," *Rural Research CSIRO*, June, 1969

Near some Gidyea trees where in days
of yore the red kangaroo could camp,
Stands a chiller box with a bloodstained
door and scales near a loading ramp,
As darkness falls all the shooters bold
drive into the gathering gloom,
Where they'll earn their bloodstained
dollars cashing in on the pet-meat boom . . .
CHARLES BAINES, as quoted in *The Australian*, November 29, 1971

As in most cases in human affairs, the problem appeared to be more political than biological or ecological. The rural interests in Australia were, and perhaps rightly so, politically very powerful. In Canberra, and in the various state houses, the graziers wanted to protect their flocks and herds (read "mobs") and what the graziers wanted, they usually got.

In the area where commercial hunting occurs, virtually all the land is alienated for grazing. It will generally be conceded, I feel sure, that on agricultural and grazing land the interests of man, the producer, should be the top priority consideration—bearing in mind, of course, that we are speaking of true and long-term interests. This means that we cannot forget, and would be unwise to try and dismiss, the past (or potential past) factor in the kangaroo equation, for effective conservation of kangaroos can only be achieved with the co-operation, or at any rate the acquiescence, of the rural community.
— FRANCIS RATCLIFFE: "The Commercial Hunting of Kangaroos," Australian Conservation Foundation, *Occasional Publication No. 4*, Melbourne, July, 1970

If this seemed like a strange statement by a conservationist, it was somewhat assuaged by later comments from the same writer, perhaps showing the kind of balanced thinking that might be applied to the kangaroo problem (and to many others, as well).

More than anyone else, outback landholders who fear kangaroos as competitors to their stock, and who exert considerable influence on government policy, hold the key to the solution of the problem. They favour commercial hunting because it provides an insurance that kangaroos will never again build up to serious pest levels; but if the industry is to survive in such a way that it is able to cope with any threatened massive breed-up of the animals, it must be provided, year in and year out, with a population of an overall moderate level from which to derive its bread and butter and enable it to maintain its markets. Such a population can only be maintained with the cooperation of graziers.
— FRANCIS RATCLIFFE: "The Commercial Hunting of Kangaroos," Australian Conservation Foundation, *Occasional Publication No. 4*, Melbourne, July, 1970

A diversion, of course, but it is remotely relevant to the problem of the kangaroos which may be the shadow image of much larger problem-solving problems in the Australian mind.

The conservation of an animal (speaking of kangaroos) which at one and the same time is a potential pest, a valuable economic resource, and a much loved component of the native fauna, has rarely, if ever, been satisfactorily achieved. Its achievement here would be a real feather in Australia's cap and would earn a worldwide acclaim.
— FRANCIS RATCLIFFE. "The Commercial Hunting of Kangaroos," Australian Conservation Foundation, *Occasional Publication No. 4,* Melbourne, July, 1970

A reasonable solution, it seemed, would be to find some systems of wild farming, or mixed farming, that would enable the indigenous species and the imported species to live together on the same area of land. All species could be harvested according to market conditions, and all species could be kept alive. Such a system would require a new way of thinking for the Australians.

The CSIRO researchers believe that the species could best be preserved on grazing land in co-existence with sheep and cattle . . .
An obvious solution is to devise methods of management that allow sheep and kangaroos to live together in a dual grazing system. Harvesting of the kangaroos would be controlled so that they did not compete seriously with the sheep. Enlightened stocking would maintain the grassland in good order; any reduction in sheep grazing might be compensated for by income from harvesting of the kangaroos. An alternative is overstocking and uncontrolled grazing of the natural grasslands to a crash point beyond which neither sheep and cattle nor kangaroos will survive.
— "Learning to Live With Kangaroos," *Rural Research,* CSIRO, June, 1969

Why spend so much time and effort pondering the problem of the kangaroos? For one thing, it was a relatively clearcut problem and the way in which the Australians went about solving it in the next thirty years or so might reveal the way they resolve much more complex problems; such as the relationship between the cen-

tral government and the state and territorial governments; future relationships to Asia, India, Indo-China, North America, Europe and Russia, at political, economic and social levels.

It was an important question because no other white-dominated country in the world had the options. The other countries had already nearly destroyed their environments beyond the point of no return.

For the Australians, in most fields, the options were still open. To exercise them would take new political structures, new economic systems, new international relationships. But most difficult of all, it would take new ways of thinking; whole new attitudes that differed from those they inherited from the bloodthirsty Western European mind.

It was not the kangaroo that was the problem, except as acting as a lens for Australian thinking, but the whole question of whether the Australians, a young, virile, pragmatic people with enormous natural and technological resources, could learn from the mistakes of the past and thus head the world into different, and perhaps better, directions.

The kangaroos were not just the symbol of a nation, but their survival was challenge to the ingenuity of a whole culture.

To be or not to be; that was the question. And, in the long run, perhaps for all life on earth.

There was the question of the Angora goats. They were important because the mohair harvested from them had an inter-

119

national market as a means of enriching the textile use of ordinary wool. (Australia was fourth in the panoply of mohair production, following South Africa, the U.S.A. and Turkey; all selling to textile manufacturers on a worldwide basis the "Golden Fleece" of the Angora.)

But traditional graziers, absorbed with Merino sheep, did not take kindly to goats, which, they felt, competed with their stock for food in the pasturage.

The goat people claim . . . that on many properties goats can be run in addition to sheep, not instead of them. Merinos typically graze herbage less than 10 inches high, whereas Angoras browse on bushes and rough stuff that are from 10 to 60 inches high. It is claimed, indeed, that the goats can return their value if only used to check Eucalyptus regrowth on recently cleared country of which there are hundreds of thousands of acres.
— The Bulletin, March 4, 1972

Some market analysts believed that an increase in Mohair production in Australia would be welcomed by other competing nations because it could help stabilize world prices and—by guaranteeing an ample supply—could lead textile manufacturers to increase their facilities for the use of the fiber.

Whatever the merits of the case, scientific research seemed to indicate that properly managed mixed farming of Angoras could, over a period of time, increase the profits of the graziers.

Other kinds of mixed farming showed promise, too. There seemed to be no reason why sheep and cattle could not be run on the same pasture, and in some places they already did. Experimental studies by the CSIRO near Canberra and by the Victorian Department of Agriculture at Rutherglen seemed to show:

Sheep and cattle grazing together can make better use of pasture than when either are grazed alone, particularly at high stocking rates . . .
Sheep did better when run with cattle than when run by themselves at equivalent stocking rates . . .
— The Daily Telegraph, February 10, 1972

So now, in thirty years' time, it might be that some extensive acreage in Australia might be devoted to mixed pastures of sheep, cattle, goats and kangaroos. Anyone left behind?

How about the water buffalo? At least in Queensland they thrive very well and might even do well in the great arc from Perth to Darwin, where the climate is much the same:

There is a breed of grazier on the Australian horizon—the buffalo man—who could eventually outdo the sheep and cattle raisers.
Experiments in Brisbane show that the long ignored buffalo produces leaner, better tasting meat, is tick resistant and can live on country too poor to support cattle . . .
The things we have been seeking in cattle we might have right on our doorstep in buffalo . . .
— The Australian, December 5, 1971

Not everyone thought that way, however. There were Australians with quite different views, including even a Darwin "conservationist" who wanted the Government to charter helicopter "gunships" for the slaughter of buffaloes in the Northern Territory.

Unless there is a drastic reduction in the buffalo population, we are going to see a major ecological catastrophe . . . The Federal Government should make helicopters equipped with heavy automatic weapons available to crews of licensed hunters.
I'm not talking about taking a few pot shots. Ninety or 95 percent of the buffaloes should be killed off to protect the environment . . . He said the buffalo carcasses would have to be left to rot. There aren't the facilities or the market.
— The Age, November 6, 1972

Well, it could be a substitute for the war. But it left some questions unanswered. To one who had scanned the Northern Territory from bush plane and land rover; from trains and automobiles a number of times in different years and different seasons, and had never seen a water buffalo except inside of a compound in a zoo, this seemed like a strange statement. From scientific reports, it was hard to see how buffaloes could damage the environment any more than did the hundreds of thousands of cattle that roamed the station properties in the Northern Territory.

But the issue itself—buffalo or five-percent buffalo—was not important. The episode showed an important ingredient of the Australian mind, which it shared with most of the rest of humankind: if you can't sell it, kill it—and leave it to rot.

He didn't say—this conservationist—why there "aren't the facilities or the market" to sell the dead buffalo, nor why they hadn't been created, nor why they could not be created before the decimation began. But that was one more facet of a part of the Australian mind; it had not realized that production, harvesting and

AGRISEARCH

Grazing goats among the sheep

FOR A MAN with a very short name, Mr S. Y. Ip, an economist in CSIRO's Industrial and Physical Sciences Branch, has touched off what threatens to become a very long argument. After studying world price and consumption trends for mohair, the fleece of the Angora goat, he has announced that, "it

accent

NAN HUTTON on FRIDAY

Let them alone where buffalo roam

THE powerfully-built man squatting on his heels in the shade was my cousin John.

The lanky fellow towelling his wet, tanned back, was Joe, the buffalo hunter, and Joe's mate, Fred, was still splashing in the blue lagoon below the grassy slope where we all waited for John and Joe to get to the point.

The point was that we had lost a wheel from John's jeep on the track from Munmalary Station, a buffalo preserve, to Mt. Bundy, the most mechanised of the five buffalo properties west of Arnhem Land.

BATS, disturbed, flew above us, and we shivered even as we came out into bright sunlight. The silence of Oenpelli is eerie. It was reassuring to find, around a rock outcrop, the camp of a woman anthropologist who was sifting methodically through the detritus of old cooking fires, quiet unperturbed about her isolation in the wilderness.

She was practical, took the magic as part of her job, and was simply intent on piercing pre-history into a pattern.

She was aware, however, of the beauty and the

He wants helicopter 'gunships' to slaughter NT buffalo

MIXED GRAZING HAS BASIC SIGNIFICANCE

ONE FRIDAY afternoon several weeks ago some grey kangaroos, two bucks, two does and a joey, were taken

sentatives Select Committee on Wildlife Conservation recommended the establishment of large reserves for kangaroos. Recent efforts by the NPWS

121

Under the tree I raised my tent,
Under the shining leaves;
The winds of life came there then spent,
Under those shining leaves.

Under the tree I set my tent,
And when at last the night was come,
Under the tree I laid me down,
Knowing that I was home.

THE DISINHERITED, XII, p. 260
Mary Gilmore Selected Verse
Angus & Robertson, 1948

PRO HART

marketing were parts of a fluid process. There seems to be a tendency to think of things in parochial ways, and to think not of processes but of neatly labeled "things." They were not alone in this, of course, but such a way of thinking could be fatal. And not only to the buffalo.

Helicopter gunships or not, one might finally come up with a farm mix of sheep, goats, cattle, kangaroos and water buffaloes, all living off the same land and seldom (except during the drought) competing for food with one another. Running such a menage would take a computer; but Australia has an abundance of computers, and talented people to run them.

A natural concomitant of mixed farming would be an overabundance of birds: mostly parrots, cockatoos and galahs. Since these were highly prized in other parts of the world, they could be harvested just like the livestock, alive though, and thus be an additional source of revenue for the farmer. It was true that their export, along with that of the lyrebird, koala and platypus were forbidden by law, except under certain circumstances (accredited zoos and such). But laws are made by men; they can be changed by men.

When the bird population rose to pest proportions, or was exceeding the ability of the farm environment, the birds could (under a revised law) be harvested alive, using traps or nets, for sale to zoos, pet stores and private collectors in other coun-tries. There should be some profit and the species would be kept alive, perhaps to breed in other parts of the world and thus expand the bird gene reservoir.

Seemingly a small thing in the way of income, but life—particularly the farmer's life—was made up of small things and even a little cash income for the farmer could go a long way. Where most societies failed was not in the grandiose government policies and schemes, but the lack of attention to the small details of day-to-day living for the "common man" who was quite literally the person everyone else lived off. This neglected person deserved a "fair go" and in thirty years might even get it. But he would have to be able and willing to think differently than he had been taught to, in school and at home, and be ready to accept new ideas that would take advantage of the new-world technologies available to him.

One wild life problem whose ultimate solution could reveal much about the Australian mind was the dingo. This half-wild dog might have been introduced into Australia by migrants from India about 6,000 years ago. After the virtual obliteration of the aboriginals who brought the dingo there, it had become completely wild and sometimes hunted in packs, like the Indian wolves from which it may have descended. Sometimes it killed and ate lambs or sheep, a privilege allowed only to man under the law.

Still it was a rare animal, possibly helping to keep down the rabbit population in some areas and, in any event, like any wild animal entitled to live out its own life in its own way, unmolested by man. There were still some pockets of dingoes remaining in Australia and sharply divided thoughts about what to do about them. Here, again, the problem was of no great significance (except to the dingo, of course) but, as in the case of the kangaroos, the water buffalo, and many other wildlife species of both flora and fauna, the *way* in which the Australians approached, and perhaps solved the problem, did seem to be important to how they might solve much larger problems that would face them by the end of the 20th Century.

A characteristic Australian attitude toward the dingo had been expressed by a man from Puddleduck who was director of the Upper Hunters' Pastures Production Board and its representative on the Lower North Coast and Tableland's Dingo Destruction Board. As far as he was concerned the only good dingo was a dead one, thus echoing a centuries-old saying of the white Americans about the native Indians and the 19th Century white Australians about the aborigines. This person said:

Even a rabbit has more appeal, and God knows they aren't worth much. But at least you can eat a rabbit; you don't eat dingoes. The dog is absolutely useless—he's a mangy, destructive animal.
—As quoted by COLIN ALLISON in *The Sydney Morning Herald,* December 8, 1971

But the other Australian point of view was expressed by an official of the National Parks and Wildlife Service who said:

Overseas, every effort is made to conserve predators and maintain the balance of nature—lions in Africa and the wolves of North America and Europe, for example. It seems to me that the protection of the dingo, and even the fox, in Australian national parks . . . would be a thoroughly worthwhile proposition.
—As quoted by COLIN ALLISON in *The Sydney Morning Herald,* December 8, 1971

It would seem that there must be some middle ground between the polarities, and that if the Australians could find it, even in the case of the lowly dingo, it would be a valuable contribution, as a methodology, for other countries facing similar problems —not to mention of some value to the dingoes.

What might be done with the mixed farming of indigenous and imported domestic animals might also be done with mixtures of native and imported plants. So far, not much had been done along these lines.

Some imported plants such as "Paterson's Curse," Scotch broom and gorse had proved disastrous. Having no natural predators in Australia, they had spread like a brush-fire, and much valuable grazing land had been taken over by them. "Paterson's Curse," which turned green paddocks into fields of purple blossoms, was edible by domestic livestock, but it tainted the milk and meat so that they were unacceptable for marketing. Scotch broom and gorse, originally imported to make the landscapes in Australia and New Zealand and New Guinea more closely resemble that of the 19th Century Scotland and England, not only proliferated very fast, but could not easily be eradicated (just like Asiatic bamboo) and thus they became "pest" plants.

There seemed to be some sort of analogy between the introduction of the plants and the introduction of West European dogs and cats, as well as rabbits. In some parts of the country, the dogs had gone wild and hunted in packs; in other parts, the domesticated cats had gone wild and hunted alone. Lambs were the usual prey, but many smaller and unique Australian fauna also were.

In these cases, the Australians apparently had not bothered to learn the lessons of other people's pasts; they only had to learn the lessons of their own past. The introduction of new species into a strange environment always carried the danger that the species might "run wild," plant or animal. This lesson could have been learned from the Egyptians, the North Americans, or virtually any other historically described culture. That the lesson had not been learned was now a matter of the past; perhaps in the future, the lesson could be learned.

It might be possible to control imported run-wilds through the introduction of insect predators, providing long-range, controlled programs showed that the predators themselves did not become a pest. It could

Growing eucalypts for wood chips

The chips are really down in Australia as the pulpwood industry responds to the Japanese demand for short-fibred wood, such as our eucalypts, with contracts signed for annual exports of 2·5 million tons of chips. Renewed interest now centres on better ways of producing pulpwood, and perhaps the concept of coppice-grown eucalypts has the most exciting possibilities. Successive crops of young stems are harvested from one stump until the sprouting ability of the stump falls below an acceptable level.

Australian phalaris has not changed

Australian phalaris has hardly evolved at all since its introduction into this continent some 90 years ago, but two recently released cultivars could cause contamination. It should therefore be managed under a pedigree certification scheme.

126

be that the introduction of viruses could control the spread of unwanted plants. Providing they did not permanently harm the environment, some types of chemical control might be used. Or through the application of genetic engineering, the offending species could be modified and thus be no longer offending, or displaced by specially "engineered" plant life that would have a higher survival potential and would have some uses for man as well.

All of these approaches had been explored to a certain extent, but not on a very large nor long-term basis. Within the next thirty years, these programs, and combinations of them, could be pursued with somewhat greater vigor. In Australia, at least there was still land enough and time to explore a number of options created by the new technologies. What was learned could be passed on to other countries with similar problems and this would be another contribution the Australians could make to the growing world consciousness.

A much greater man-introduced problem was clearing the native trees to make room for the grazing of sheep and cattle. The trees—mostly eucalypts—were "ringed," i.e., the bark was cut all around the trunk, thus killing the tree. When the tree died, it

By COLIN ALLISON

National park's dingo colony sparks debate

A COLONY of dingoes living in the rugged Barrington Tops National Park is embarrassing local graziers and causing friction between two government organisations.

Graziers say the dingoes are breeding in the park, 65 miles north-west of Newcastle, and raiding nearby sheep country.

The Lower North Coast and Tablelands Dingo Destruction Board is keen to destroy the dingoes by dropping poisoned liver from the air, but the National Parks and Wildlife Service (NPWS) believes the animals are already kept under control in the park.

Mr H. W. Carter, a grazier, of "Woodburn," said about 100 head of stock had been killed in the past 12 months by marauding dingoes, mainly in the Stuart Brook area west of the sanctuary.

"This year they came down out of the Tops into settled country where they haven't been seen for 70 or 80 years," he said.

"We organised a drive a couple of weeks ago, but dogs are smart and we managed to shoot only one. Another which escaped was killed later, but there are plenty left."

However, Mr W. Steel, assistant director of the NPWS, denied that the 34,500-acre park was a dingo breeding ground.

A ranger sent in recently found no evidence of a big buildup in the dingo population, he said. Actually, the number of dogs taken from the district had decreased in recent years.

"The dingoes could just as easily be moving in from adjacent crown land as from the parkland," he said.

Mr Steel stressed that dingoes were not being protected in the park, but were being watched. "Our own staff is capable of controlling them," he said. "We are definitely against aerial baiting as proposed by the wild dog board."

Aerial baiting was unselective and its overall effects were still unknown. The subject was being studied by the CSIRO.

Mr R. Taylor, of "Puddledock," Ellerston, a director of the Upper Hunter Pastures Protection Board and the board's representative on the Lower North Coast and Tablelands Dingo Destruction Board, said the DDB was charged by an Act of Parliament with "continuously surveying and destroying dingoes, declared noxious animals."

He said control was not being carried out in the park.

"I live nearby and I know they are breeding there," he said.

"Generally throughout the tablelands the DDB has kept dingoes down in recent years. Where 15 years ago we paid out bonuses on the scalps of up to 1,500 dingoes a year, now it's down to 450 or so annually. But in the Barrington Tops there are just as many dogs as ever."

Mr Taylor said the NPWS was not sympathetic to the landholder, who was already plagued with economic problems. The service was interested in protecting wild dogs, regardless of what it said to the contrary.

As far as Mr Taylor is concerned the only good dingo is a dead one.

"Even a rabbit has more appeal, and God knows they aren't worth much," he said. "But at least you can eat a rabbit, you don't eat dingoes. The dog is absolutely useless — he's a mangy, destructive animal."

One NPWS official, who wished to remain anonymous, said dingoes should be protected in parks.

"Overseas, every effort is made to conserve predators and maintain the balance of nature — lions in Africa and the wolves of North America and Europe, for example," he said.

"It seems to me that the protection of the dingo, and even the fox, in Australian national parks like Barrington Tops would be a thoroughly worthwhile proposition."

A dingo. "Even a rabbit has more appeal."

Experts rate buffalo as big income earner

THERE is a breed of grazier on the Australian horizon — the buffalo man — who could eventually outdo the sheep and cattle raisers.

"The things we have been seeking in cattle we might have right on our doorstep in the buffalo," Mr Johnson said last week.

Experiments in Brisbane show that the long-ignored buffalo produces leaner, better tasting meat, is tick-resistant and can live on country too poor to support cattle, buffalo given free by Mount Bundey station and Mudginberre developers in the Northern Territory are being shipped to Brisbane for the project.

Queensland University has had a small herd of buffalo for three years at its Moggill experimental farm.

Beats ticks

For a beginning Mr Charles sees the buffalo as the ideal beast to run on gonna country — a buffalo/beef producer to survive in unimproved or marginal type cattle country.

buffalo with ticks the students have found one adult tick on 20 buffaloes."

Mr Charles said buffalo meat was high in muscle content and low in fat — the ideal meat for the U.S. market. The buffalo could survive on low quality forage in poor country and still put on 1½lb a day.

Then what is the catch?

"The catch appears to be a slow growth rate," he said. "But we have been experimenting in the worst circumstances — starting with animals not selectively bred and without a choice of the best animals available."

was cut down and the remains were piled in huge windrows and then burned. Why, at a time and in a country that had to import most of its combustible fuel, the trees could not have been used in suitably designed stoves for cooking and in fire-places for heating, is a mystery not likely to be solved. But the stoves were designed in England for burning coal (later natural gas, or for using electricity); it was the English way of doing things, and another example of the grain or set of the Australian mind.

No matter what was done with the wood, windrows or stove burning, the ultimate effect was the same. In many areas, the land was virtually stripped of trees to make room for pasturage; the natural watershed system was destroyed and there was no shade for the livestock during the hot seasons. The green pasturage, cut low by grazing sheep, often could not contend with the sudden, violent rainstorms, and the result was ugly, red gulleys of erosion, not fit for man or beast.

While it was not too late, other practices might be tried. There was one being tried in the central New Guinea highlands that might offer a partial answer to the depreda-tion of English farming methods. In New Guinea, in the virgin hardwood forests, the trees were selectively cut, leaving lanes

open for trucks and other agricultural machinery. The livestock browsed or grazed between the trees, cutting down the undergrowth and not only finding forage, but greatly reducing the threat of bushfires. The remaining trees held the watershed intact to help prevent erosion, provided shade for the livestock, which in hot weather periods was important to maintain growth, weight and marketing values of cattle.

Of course, the central highlands of New Guinea and the timbered areas of the Southeastern coastal areas of Australia were not the same, but there were many similarities of temperature, climate and rainfall. Perhaps for some still undeveloped areas of Australia, a livestock-pasturage-tree system could still be worked out.

Again in New Guinea's highlands, two new trees were being planted for every old one cut down. The chief forester, a New Zealander, had said, "We're in a thousand year business. To be so, we have to protect the forest, not rape it."

He pointed out that newly planted soft-woods could be harvested in 17 to 20 years; the hardwoods in 90. The softwoods would be processed into plywood for export throughout Australasia; the hard-woods had a worldwide market. The livestock hides and carcasses were trucked to Lae and then shipped to Japan where they commanded premium prices.

Such a mixed-farm scheme might work in some parts of Australia; worth looking into before all the eucalyptus (there were more than 600 species) died in their tracks with a ring around their trunks. Dead white sepulchres, their arms supplicating a changing world.

Somehow the white man had never learned to do much with eucalyptus, the mulga and mallee, but the black man did; he left them alone.

Except, of course, for occasional black man-set bushfires to drive out the bandicoots and other small game, which could then be clubbed to death as they fled the ring of fire; or picked up—in the case of field mice and lizards—ready to eat, roasted in the still-hot ashes. But the fire scarcely gave the gum trees a good summer tan; like vacationers at the beach, they would be back. The trees the European settlers cut down could never come back.

There had been some talk of harvesting the widespread mulga for a woodchip, particle board industry, but not much had come of it, as yet. A suitably managed mulga harvesting could preserve the species, and reduce some of the bush-fire danger.

Any of these mixed processes involved a different way of thinking. For any culture on earth, thinking differently would be very difficult. Whether the Australians were willing or able to do it was an open question. But at least it *was* an open question. Few, if any, other cultures had such an opportunity. It would be interesting in the next thirty years or so to see if the Australians would exercise it.

No one knows precisely why whole groups of plants and animals periodically vanish or what factors are most significant in conferring superiority to one species over another. Large-scale extinctions, however, seem to result whenever two pockets of evolution are opened up to one another after long isolation. For this reason, Australia offers modern science the chance of an eon—a confrontation between native creatures and outsiders which, in its continental scope, is not likely to be matched for tens of millions of years.
—*The Land and Wildlife of Australia:* by David Bergamini and the editors of LIFE. Time, Incorporated, New York (c) 1964

The animals and the plants could, under proper human management, reproduce themselves indefinitely. This did not appear to be true of the mineral, metal and chemical resources. Once removed from the continent, they could not be replaced. Of course, on a global scale, they would always be there; in city dumps and the remains of abandoned cars in otherwise empty lots, and in time, would come back. But that was not of much use to the Australians, not in the short span of thirty years, anyway.

One could look at it in another way. Think of rocks as "living" things. They were, after all, created, born, changed form and in dying, changed forms once again. It was only the time span that was different; it was, by human standards, too long to count them as "living beings." But that was a human judgment. Rocks did not reproduce themselves sexually, as humans did, but they reproduced themselves in another way, as any geologist could explain.

When one put all these things together, a sort of opportunity pattern emerged. Suppose one thought of the whole area— New Guinea, Australia, New Zealand and Antarctica and the seas and reefs and islands that surrounded them— as a vast laboratory for the world. The facilities were magnificent. Lots of space. Highly competent people.

New Guinea:

There were, in New Guinea, facilities for studying tropical rain forests, duplicating similar environmental conditions in South America and Africa.

Here, one could study the ticks in the high grasses on the slopes and plateaus and find out how they affected humans and livestock, and how possibly to control them.

One could study virtually unpolluted river systems, without the variants of human pollution which greatly complicated the problem elsewhere.

One could study the complexities of human behavior in tribal situations almost uncontaminated by Western philosophies and technological inputs. This could be a sort of social psychiatry—the dreamtime of thousands of years muttered in hundreds of different languages. The *sotto voce* of mankind's heritage. One could learn something about oneself, but one would have to hurry; the missionaries, and government bureaucrats and traders were preparing a mass penetration. So little time left.

Still, it could be done.

Such studies could, of course, be done in Africa, South America or Micronesia. And some had been, but they were scattered and inconclusive and most of them were conducted without the technological advantages of such tools as tape recorders, motion pictures, video tape and computer data processing, and the application of what is so far known through the application of behavioral science and general systems techniques.

The people of New Guinea were an endangered species—endangered by the intrusion of white European cultures and Aristotelian philosophies. These tribal people were unique. Perhaps in the next 30 years a "proper study of mankind" could be made of them, on an international scale as a contribution toward the understanding of all humans of themselves.

Then, too, one considered that much of New Guinea had not been scientifically and rigorously explored for natural resources. Yet if Australia had been able to reveal so much of "hidden" resources in a mere 150 years through relatively primitive means of exploration, what might New Guinea yield with the proper use of contemporary technological tools?

True, New Guinea was not a part of Australia in the nationalistic and political sense. But, then, nationalism was a political fossil that would largely have been relegated to a museum of human mistakes within a decade or so.

What seemed important was that Australia was the closest technological country to New Guinea and, therefore, among the nations of the world in the most favorable position to arrange for, supervise, monitor and make available to other nations the wealth of information that could be developed only there.

Australians could think of it as a great natural resource, not for exploitation, but as a unique laboratory for exploration—the results from which could have a great significance to the more ideological, European concepts that dominate the tropical and semi-tropical areas of the world.

It would cost so little—it could yield so much.

New Zealand:

Now, New Zealand was not, politically, a part of Australia, either. But its geographic proximity, its parallel cultural development, its ethnic and lingual similarity, made it, no matter what the politicians in Canberra and more importantly, Wellington might say, a part of Australia—in the sense that all of Australia was a single geographic and economic entity, and Australia was the pivot.

Now, looking around in a kind of desultory way, one found New Zealanders running mines, timber operations, cattle stations, banks and businesses in Australia. One also found Australians building dams and power stations, aluminium plants and frozen lamb loading operations in New Zealand.

Sure, there were differences—so subtle that only an Australian could tell who was a New Zealander, and vice versa. So, no matter how one looked at it, New Zealand had to be a part of the Australian complex, too.

New Zealand?—"Here be monsters." Vast resources of falling water turning turbines. Lakes so large one could not see the other shores—Te Anau and Manapouri among them. Fjords such as Doubtful Sound and Milford Sound. There were mountains so high that the congealed breath of Antarctica never melted. There were windows to the center of the earth where steam reared up like the exhalation of fiery dragons. Long green meadows where the flocks of sheep roamed like clouds across an upside-down emerald sky.

On South Island were the climatic and geologic counterparts of Scandinavia, Newfoundland, Nova Scotia, Alaska, parts of northern Canada, of Russia, Siberia, China and Manchuria.

The land area of New Zealand (both islands) was reckoned at 103,736 square miles but that did not include the Ross Dependency on Antarctica (160,000 square miles) for a total of 263,736 square miles. There weren't many people in that area, a little over 2,800,000, not much more than the population of Australia's Sydney.

So, there was plenty of room in New Zealand to try out all sorts of longterm experiments, possibly sponsored by other countries that could not realistically be performed by them because of ideological, religious, political or racial restraints. The New Zealanders probably would hardly notice the newcomers and such experiments could be of immense value to a world community groping through the murk toward the 21st Century. And, of course, a prime source of income.

The ultra-conservative New Zealanders might not take too kindly to the notion, but they were an eminently pragmatic people, and if a scheme made money and did not change their lifestyle, why not give it a go?

Antarctica:

One had already examined the possible use of Antarctica as the world's largest fridge—it rounded out Australia's capabilities, still unexploited, to explore concepts for atomic waste disposal, for cryogenic experiments in medicine, electronics, space equipment and instrumentation and possibly for a new dimension in international tourism.

Again, from a political standpoint, Antarctica was not a "part" of Australia. But Australians (and New Zealanders) largely led the expeditions that explored Antarctica and the two governments had jurisdiction over very large areas there. Here was a place where the Australians could lead the way; no other people knew more about this last, lost continent (except, perhaps, the Russians).

In Antarctica, for the Australians, there seemed to be everything to gain and nothing to lose in the next three decades.

The Great Barrier Reef:

As every school child knew by now, the Reef was by far the largest formation of its kind in the world. It lay along the eastern Australian coast like a giant sea snake (all 1,250 miles of it) basking in warm, shallow water.

It dozed in its million-year Pleistocene sleep, content with its condominium of finny, scaly, furry, blobby occupants, most of whom had been in residence for millions of years.

The water that surrounded it was warm as blood, as clear as crystal. The bait fish darted like schools of silver bullets, missiles that somehow escaped the giant game fish that roamed off-shore. The enormous groupers pouted in the slowly waving coral fans, the sea urchins clustered in little black spiny communities, waiting for the next tide. Stonefish waited stolidly, and sting rays carpeted the shallows in arrays of diamond shapes. The surf pounded like freight trains crashing on the outer edges of the reef.

Considering the importance of coral reefs throughout the tropical and subtropical world—off the Fijis, the Hawaiian Islands, the West Indies, South America, Africa, the Red Sea, the western Indian Ocean and off Indonesia, one would think that perhaps Australia's Great Barrier Reef could serve as a giant, world laboratory for those countries and continents that had their own reefs, but not the technological abilities (at least not now) to perform studies on such subjects as:

Sea life in all its tropical and subtropical forms; wave action measurements and the development of wave action theory, tidal phenomena, methods for the conservation of sea life and possible controlled commercial production of edible varieties in large quantities—much like the deliberate culturation of oysters, clams, mussels and abalone in other parts of the world.

Except for its vast size, the Reef does not differ in any significant way from coral reefs in other places on the planet. It has habitable islands where permanent laboratory facilities could be installed, and most of the Reef lies only a relatively short distance from the mainland. The Reef itself provided sheltered water so that, most of the year, even small boats could navigate safely.

What more could one ask?

Assuming—just assuming—that it was possible for the Australians to create a laboratory for the world.

Assuming—just assuming—that all the resources existed, and there was plenty of evidence that they did exist.

Assuming—just assuming—that other countries of the world were genuinely interested in experimenting with and conducting longterm studies that they could not—for political, ethnic, cultural, religious, social, technological or ideological reasons —carry out themselves.

Assuming all that—then how could the Australians make it possible for them to conduct these experiments?

The Australians already knew how but they did not know that they did. They had not really thought out the global implications of what they already had done so well.

It has been said that the only failure is success. But who can define either failure or success? Well, one could assume that

one goal of humans was to live comfortably without hurting anyone else and to enjoy their daily lives on a beautiful planet with the minimum disturbance of its natural beauty.

To some extent, and with some realistic reservations, most Australians had already done this very well.

Could not this expertise in lifestyles be made available to countries and cultures that were not so abundantly endowed? One thought it could.

But how? How?

Now, one could consider that it was at least possible, if not probable, that the Australians might decide that their role in the future could be to serve as a vast laboratory for the world.

Let one assume that the decision would be made to do so.

Where in the world was there the organizational ability to put such a complicated scheme together and make it work?

Funny thing was, they already had it.

There were two ongoing systems which if merged could pull off the whole thing.

These two systems, or organizations, were the Commonwealth Scientific and Industrial Organization—usually referred to as CSIRO—and the Department of National Development—now called the Department of Minerals and Energy. These were two extraordinary organizations without a parallel in the world.

They were interdisciplinary and not beholden to any particular political administration nor to the military. Their allegiance, not only theoretically, but actually, was to applications of "pure science" to the needs of the people.

Take them one at a time.

Choose CSIRO only because one had to choose one or the other as a starter. In the Australian game of "two up," one chose heads or tails, didn't one?

Heads it is and CSIRO is it, and the game is on.

What is a CSIRO?

It is a giant creature that roams the Australian world in seven-league boots. The today counterpart of Gulliver, it is equally at home—and equally curious and perceptive in Lilliput or Brobdingnag.

One could take a stroll with this giant and feel something of its strengths and perhaps something of its weaknesses. But the trip would at least be interesting, and perhaps provocative. Who knows what one might find in the morning of the world?

Something about CSIRO can be found out from the study of a modest little pamphlet which was a sort of preview of the real thing.

One read aloud in the quiet of the morning watch from this little folder tucked away in the chart room. In doing so, one anticipated the relief of the watch and the dawn of a new day.

Here it is from CSIRO: call it Seero for short, although the Australian crew always spelled it out—C...S...I...R...O; something like that novel called M*A*S*H.

No matter, one was alone in the cold of that morning and standing there on the wing of the bridge, watched for the reefs ahead, it was at least something to fill in the time.

It went something like this:

"CSIRO is not a government department, but an instrumentality set up by an Act of Parliament . . . The Executive is responsible to Parliament through the Minister for Education and Science.

"Of CSIRO's income (over $46,000,000 per annum) three quarters are provided for in the Commonwealth Budget. The remainder is contributed to CSIRO by woolgrowers, the cattle industry, the dairy industry, the tobacco industry, the wheat industry and other donors representing every branch of Australian primary and secondary industry . . .

"The scientific staff includes 1,000 research scientists, supported by 800 other professional scientists. The total staff is more than 6,000.

"The fields of work covered are immensely varied. Some of CSIRO's contributions are well known:

"The addition of certain trace elements to soils in southern Australia had transformed semi-desert into rich grazing land, carrying improved pastures."

(Wouldn't this be of some interest to the people of Africa and the Middle East and

India? One thought it might be. The climatic and geologic conditions were much the same; but the Raft had space enough and time, plus the technological inheritance of more than 8,000 years.)

To go on:

"The introduction of myxomatosis reduced the rabbit scourge to a fraction of its size and paved the way for tremendous increases in primary production.

"Less well known, but almost as spectacular, has been the elimination or control of diseases which ravaged crops and herds.

"Vaccines developed by CSIRO protect sheep from black disease and enterotoxaemia and cattle from brucellosis and pleuro-pneumonia. Entomologists have reduced the damage done by insects such as termites, weevils, locusts and cattle ticks.

"Possibly the best known work in the wool textile industry is concerned with new processes developed by CSIRO to allow wool to be shrink-proofed, moth-proofed, permanently pleated, and given 'wash-and-wear' properties.

"It is perhaps not so widely known that CSIRO discovered how to use Australian hardwoods in paper manfacture, thereby laying the foundations for a whole industry.

"Neither is it well known that all Australian commercial aircraft carry Distance Measuring Equipment invented by CSIRO radar scientists, nor that CSIRO scientists have succeeded in completely mechanizing the once laborious process of cheddar cheese manufacture."

From cheddar to radar is one giant step, but this modern-day Gulliver already had made it, and one foot was firmly set in the 21st Century.

Well, that little brochure was certainly good enough, but it did not really describe the extraordinary range of CSIRO activities.

Poking around in the Raft's chartroom, one came across, in a hop, skip and jump away, some of the highways and byways of research this almost unbelievable creature was snuffling along.

The excerpts, read in the dim, predawn light of the 21st Century, were from on old (1969) CSIRO annual report.

Some of them went like this:

Projects already terminated included:

Atlas of Australian Soils: This has been a major project by the Division of Soils. It has extended over ten years and has involved the preparation of a key to the major soils of Australia and a considerable amount of field work. The work has been completed and the maps published.

Transport of Meat and Fruit: The Physics Section of the Division of Food Preservation has been engaged in work on problems associated with changes in methods of exporting meat and fruit to overseas markets . . . The work has been completed and the recommendations have been turned over to commercial organizations for implementation to other physical problems associated with cold storage.

Irrigation Research: A project at the Division of Irrigation Research on the influence of transpiration of water from plants on the timing of irrigation has been terminated . . .

Keeping Quality of Butterfat: An investigation into this problem by the Division of Dairy Research came to a successful end when the relationship between the copper content, pH, and keeping quality of butterfat during butter manufacture was determined . . . The research team is now concentrating on the centralized production of deep-frozen cheese starter concentrates to supply the cheese industry.

Genetics and Breeding of Soya Beans: This project came to an end when the officer concerned left the Division of Tropical Pastures to join the staff of the University of Queensland. He will continue this line of research at the University . . .

Concrete: Studies by the Division of Building Research on the steam curing of concrete and the curing conditions to maximize the strength of lightweight concrete have been successfully concluded . . . Staff and finance have been transferred to work on the use of computers for structural design.

Fuel Cells: The completion by the Division of Mineral Chemistry of work designed to provide an understanding of the chemical processes occurring within fuel cells has enabled the staff to join a team studying the genesis of ore bodies.

Inorganic Combustion Products: The Division of Mineral Chemistry is studying inorganic combustion products to overcome problems of atmospheric and fouling deposits on the heat transfer surfaces of boilers. The work has been satisfactorily concluded and the staff reallocated to the team studying ore genesis.

Electrode Processes: The commercial production of metals such as aluminium and copper generally involved an electrolytic process. A programme in the Division of Mineral Chemistry has been concerned with the properties of electrode surfaces and the mechanisms of electrode reactions. The fundamental studies have ceased and staff transferred to work on other projects, principally the chemistry of molten salts.

Fluidization: The Division of Mineral Chemistry made an investigation of the behavior of coal when burned in a fluidized bed. Successful completion of this part of the programme has enabled the staff to be reallocated to work on the flotation of sulphide ores containing carboniferous materials.

Atomic Absorption Spectroscopy: In 1968, the Industrial and Physical Sciences Branch undertook a cost benefit analysis of a novel method of chemical analysis that was developed by the Division of Chemical Physics . . . The measured benefits up to June 1968 were estimated to have a net value of $22 million and by 1978 it was expected that this figure would reach at least $120 million. The amount spent by CSIRO on research on atomic absorption up to June 1968 was $1.3 million.

Meteorological Research: Under the auspices of the Division of Meteorological Physics in cooperation with a government agency, a programme was begun to study the behavior of the atmosphere, with emphasis on its general circulation, in order to obtain better understanding of the distribution and variations in climate on the earth, and to improve the accuracy and time scale of weather forecasting.

Research on Prawns: A new programme was begun by the Division of Fisheries and Oceanography to study prawns in northern Australia and was aimed at obtaining a thorough knowledge of the biology and ecology of the various prawn species in these waters and the factors controlling their distribution and number.

There were several important points that could be established from that brief and catalogic recital.

One certainly had some idea of the tremendous versatility and variety of projects that CSIRO was willing and able to undertake. The number of successfully completed research projects was an indication that the scientific talent was there and working. The shifting of teams from completed projects to other projects in other fields showed a type of interdisciplinary flexibility not usually found in basic research organizations. There also appeared to be, as in the case of the study of atomic absorption spectroscopy, tremendous economic returns for Australia compared to the original investment.

What one had just read were entries in the Raft's log that recorded some earlier journeys that had ended successfully, as well as a sampling of a few of the new voyages just beginning.

But to get a better view of the enormous range of the Raft crew's scientific and technical abilities, one found it useful to scan some of the entries concerning the ongoing voyages through time and space.

One found them under the CSIRO label, and they went something like this:

More Water for Australia:

Over the last ten years, the Division of Soils has been attempting to measure the ground water beneath the Gambier Plain of southeastern South Australia and southwestern Victoria. Recharge of this underground water occurs during winter and spring by direct infiltration of soil water into an aquifer (a layer of porous, water conducting rock) . . . many of which are more than 300 feet thick.

The Division has estimated that the annual recharge is about half a million acre-feet, making this body of underground water by far the largest single resource of good quality water in South Australia apart from the River Murray . . . The Division has estimated that there is enough water under the Gambier Plain to irrigate up to 350,000 acres of pasture a year without exceeding the annual recharge . . .

Supplying Trace Elements to Plants:

The commonest way of overcoming a trace element deficiency in soil is to add the element as a water soluble salt mixed with a fertilizer such as super-phosphate. However, many soluble salts are easily leached from the soil . . .

A class of compounds which could provide a reliable and comparatively cheap source of trace elements for plants is now being investigated by the Division of Soils. The Division found it could produce crystalline complexes between trace elements and glycerol which were insoluble in water but were broken down by strong

oxidative and reductive reaction . . .
The complexes have been named
Sirochels . . .

Do Reeds Waste Water?:

In the Murrumbidgee Irrigation Area,
much of the excess irrigation water drains
into what has now become a large but
shallow reservoir known as Barrenbox
swamp.

During 1968, the Division of Meteorological Research was asked to determine
whether the presence of tall reeds growing
in the swamp led to increased loss of
water through evaporation.

Using an instrument called a Fluxatron,
which was developed by the Division, and
which measures evaporation directly, the
Division found the evaporation rates over
both swamp and lake were similar after
heavy rainfall, but that in the generally
prevailing conditions of the area the
presence of reeds actually inhibited
evaporation.

More Grains in the Crop:

At flowering, an ear of wheat consists of
a series of spikelets. Each spikelet contains
several small flowers or florets, some of
which later develop grains. The Division of
Plant Industry is trying to discover what
determines the number of grains in a
spikelet and the number of spikelets in an
ear. If the Division can find this out, it may
then be able to increase wheat yields by
increasing the number of grains per ear . . .

Pastures from the Air:

There are extensive areas of non-arable
land in southern Australia which receive
enough rain to support improved pastures.
Although aerial sowing of pastures has
been tried in these areas, it has not been
widely adopted because of the failure of
many temperate grasses and legumes to
establish well after surface sowing . . . The
Division of Plant Industry . . . has been
studying germination and early seedling
development in a range of commercial
pasture species to determine the factors
affecting establishment after surface
sowing.

Among other things, the results of this
work should help the Division's plant
breeders define the criteria for new
varieties of pasture plants specifically
adapted to the conditions of aerial
sowing . . .

Warm Soils Grow More Oranges:

Since 1967, the Division of Irrigation
Research has been conducting a longterm
experiment to investigate the effects of
different cultural treatments and different
levels of nitrogen fertilizer on the growth,
yield and fruit composition of Late Valencia
and Washington Navel orange trees.

To date, the best soil management practice has been to maintain a bare unculti-
vated soil surface kept free of weeds by
chemical sprays. Adequately fertilized
trees receiving this treatment have
produced higher yields of better quality
fruit than trees receiving permanent sod or
winter cover crop treatments . . . Using
bare surface culture . . . the Division has
obtained average annual yields of 20 tons
of oranges an acre . . . several times the
local average . . .

Some of the benefits of bare surface culture are thought to be due to higher root temperatures, particularly in the spring . . .

Less Grit in the Grapes:

Although dried vine fruits are washed during processing in packing sheds, it is not always possible to remove the last traces of soil that collect on the fruit during picking and drying. If too much soil remains, the fruit tastes gritty.

The recent development by the Division of Horticultural Research of a simple and inexpensive grit-measuring device has provided the dried fruit industry with a valuable tool in its campaign to improve fruit quality . . . Gritometers were used successfully on a trial basis in some packing houses in 1968 and by 1969 were used in all packing houses.

Pastures for the Dry Tropics:

The country west of the Dividing Range in tropical Queensland carries open eucalypt woodlands and tall grasses which are typical of much of northern Australia. Most of the annual rainfall of 25 inches occurs between December and March. Pasture quality declines during the dry season, reaching critically low levels in the spring. Cattle properties in the area are large, but stocking rates on unimproved country are low—about one animal to 45 acres. Steers take about six years to fatten.

Research over the last four years by the Division of Tropical Pastures has shown that much higher levels of production are possible. Clearing trees from the native pasture increases the amount of soil moisture sufficiently to double the production of grass and to allow the ready establishment of Townsville lucerne.

Pastures improved in this way have carried bullocks at one to six acres and fattened them to market weight at three years of age.

Grasses and legumes from South America and Africa are being tested . . .

Dairy Cattle for the Tropics:

European breeds of dairy cattle do not perform well in the tropics and subtropics of northern Australia, where temperature and humidity are high and parasites such as ticks are prevalent. Zebu cattle (from Pakistan) tolerate higher temperature and humidity, are more tick-resistant, and far better on poor quality dry feed, but they produce less milk than European breeds . . .

In 1956, a breeding programme to combine the most desirable qualities of both European and Zebu breeds (Jersey from Europe; Sahiwals and Red Sindhis from Pakistan).

Each bull is first tested in a hot room at Badgery's Creek to determine its ability to regulate its body temperature and maintain its appetite under hot conditions. They then are tested for tick resistance . . .

The Division's breeding programme is the only one in the world using heat tolerance and tick resistance tests as an aid to selection . . . Already the average milk yield and fat production of the crossbreds are at least equal to those of local Jerseys, while the best of the crossbreds have outyielded the best of the Jerseys. In addition, heat tolerance and tick resistance have been greatly increased . . .

"Sometimes a heavy, reptile-hostility came off the sombre land, something gruesome and infinitely repulsive."[37]
D. H. Lawrence, *Kangaroo* (Penguin ed. 1950)

Shearers Playing for a Bride—*Arthur Boyd*

Sheep That Don't Drink:

When native pastures are replaced by improved pastures, there may be less runoff of rainfall into the dams and surface tanks that supply stock with their drinking water. At the same time, stocking rates are increased, so that pasture improvement can lead to more stock but less drinking water.

The Division of Animal Physiology has undertaken research on this and is seeking the answer to a number of questions, but the main one is "How much of a sheep's requirement for drinking water can be provided by the pasture without affecting the sheep's well-being or production?"

Results so far had shown there was little difference in body weights or wool growth between those that were given water and those that were not; if anything, the sheep that did not have access to water grew more wool.

(Sheep raising countries take note!)

Selenium and Sheep Fertility:

Selenium is one of the trace elements needed by sheep in their diet. Lack of it causes disease in lambs and may cause

Merino rams are still up in the air

By JON POWIS

Thinning trees with chemicals

Instead of ring-barking standing trees or 'sucker bashing' to remove unwanted woody regrowth, graziers are now turning to chemical methods of control.

infertility in ewes. The Division of Nutritional Biochemistry, which has been studying the problem for some years, is looking into the possibility of providing sheep with a regular supply of selenium by means of a heavy pellet containing the element.

When administered to sheep, the pellet remains in the rumen where it dissolves slowly over a period of years, releasing a continuous dose of selenium.

The technique was developed by the Division some years ago to prevent cobalt deficiency in sheep and cattle and has proved so successful that some millions of cobalt pellets are now made in Australia each year . . .

Fighting the White Wax Scale:

White wax scale, a serious pest of citrus, is found along the east coast of Australia . . . A sugary secretion produced by the scales favours the growth of a black sooty mould on the fruit and leaves of citrus trees . . .

Early attempts (1935) to control the scale by introducing parasites from East Africa were unsuccessful, but in 1965 the Division of Entomology returned to the task and so far some 17 species of insects had been considered as potential agents for biological control . . . The investigation continues . . .

Finding Enemies for Skeleton Weed:

Skeleton weed, a deep rooted perennial plant native to the Mediterranean region and central and southern Europe, has been present in Australia since 1914 . . . It is a major weed of wheat crops in southeastern Australia. It reduces crop yields by competing with the wheat plants for water and nutrients, and its tough stems foul harvesting machinery.

Skeleton weed is attacked in its native habitat by a variety of insects and other organisms. If some of these could be introduced into Australia they might aid in the control of the weed . . .

The Division of Entomology, therefore, established a research station in southern France in 1966 to look for natural enemies of the skeleton weed and to study its ecology . . .

Three very promising enemies have been found so far—a fungus, a gall mite, and an aphid. The fungus infects skeleton weed seedlings in autumn and spring. When not fatal, the infection prevents or greatly reduces flowering. The gall mite attacks the flowering buds and the autumn seedlings, and the aphids attack seedlings and infest the tips of the growing flower shoots . . .

On the Track of the Dingo:

Early in 1966, the Division of Wildlife Research began a study of the ecology of the dingo. An area of nearly 10,000 square miles (almost as large as the state of Maryland in the U.S., as big as Belgium or Haiti) was studied to discover the lifestyle of the dingo.

The Division also examined the effects of aerial baiting. All permanent watering points on 18 properties covering 20,000 square miles were surveyed before and after baiting . . . Results showed clearly that the baiting was not effective. Dingo numbers fell insignificantly on six properties, including two of the three unbaited properties used as controls, but rose on all others and almost trebled on the property with the most dingoes . . .

(Thus, it was determined that aerial baiting would not solve the problem of the dingo for those graziers who considered it a threat to their flocks.)

Watch on the Wedge-Tail:

The Division of Wildlife Research has been studying the wedge-tailed eagle to obtain a detailed understanding of its biology and to measure its importance as a predator of lambs . . . A study near Canberra and in northeastern New South Wales of the eagle's food habits has shown that rabbits are the primary prey, followed by birds, small mammals, lizards and kangaroo. In both areas, lamb constituted only about 7% of the eagle's diet.

Preliminary results show clearly that the impact of predation by nesting eagles on the pastoral industry is not significant . . . Clearing of forests and the introduction of exotic animals, particularly rabbits, appear to have provided the eagles with a better habitat than they had before.

Although more than 30,000 eagles are estimated to be killed by graziers each year, the present population (of eagles) appears high enough to sustain itself.

Southern Bluefin Tuna:

The Australian tuna fishing industry is based on the southern bluefin tuna. This species occurs off the southern coasts of Africa, Australia, New Zealand and South America . . .

Since 1962, the Division of Fisheries and Oceanography has caught, tagged and released over 44,000 southern bluefin in Australian waters to obtain information on the movement of the tuna population.

The East Australian Current:

The East Australian Current is a major component of the oceanic circulation off the east coast of Australia. It is a south-flowing current and its strength is greatest about 20 miles from the coast at the edge of the continental shelf.

Changes in the flow of the Current during the year, bring about changes in the physical and chemical characteristics of the waters off the coast . . .

The Division of Meteorological Physics has found definite correlations between sea surface temperatures along the coast of New South Wales and rainfall on the mainland . . . Variations in the Current are also important for the tuna fishing industry . . .

The Division of Fisheries and Oceanography has been studying the Current to obtain a three-dimensional picture of it and to determine the volume of flow. Direct measurements of water movements at between 1300 and 3500 metres were made by tracking the movement of neutrally buoyant floats that had their density adjusted to equal that of sea water at a desired depth . . .

Keeping Rooms Cool:

A room in a house can be kept cool in hot weather by using an evaporative device which draws warm outside air into the room over a moist surface. Water evaporating from the moist surface lowers the temperature of the air.

Evaporative coolers cost less than refrigerated air-conditioning units and are cheaper to run, but even in hot, dry countries their performance is limited because they increase the humidity of the air that they cool.

The Division of Mechanical Engineering has devised a simple and compact evaporative cooler which gives lower temperatures and humidities . . .

The key to this improved performance is a plate heat exchanger; the plates being about 10/1000 of an inch thick. The unit—which includes two fans, a water pump, and water spray nozzles—is expected to give satisfactory cooling in most parts of Australia except in the humid tropics . . . Although the construction of the cooler is novel, it should be adaptable to mass production methods.

Measuring Shadows:

From a knowledge of the sun's position at different times of the year, an architect designing a house or an office building can work out the best positions and angles of any shading devices he may decide to use . . .

These calculations have now been made easier by a computer program developed jointly by the Division of Building Research and the Division of Mechanical Engineer-

ing. Using this system, a complete sun/shadow history of any part of a building can be determined . . .

How Long Does it Take?:

Unexpected delays in the construction of buildings are annoying and frustrating to all concerned and can be costly. A survey by the Division of Building Research of some 350 buildings, ranging in price from $10,000 to over $10,000,000 and excluding houses, has shown that the time taken to construct a building is on the average nearly half as long again as the time originally allowed in the contract . . .

There are a number of factors involved but the basic cause appears to be lack of information on the relationship between the size of the building, the contractual procedure and construction time.

The information being obtained by the division on these relationships is making it possible to define standards of performance that can be regarded as normal.

Predicting Soil Behavior:

In designing structures such as road pavements, building foundations, and earthen-dams, engineers need to predict the mechanical behavior of the soil under load . . .

The difficulty has been to describe the structure of a soil so that it can be related to the mechanical behavior of the soil. The Division of Soil Mechanics has developed techniques for describing and measuring both the spatial distribution and the spatial orientation of the individual particles or units of each of the three main soil components—sand and silt grains, clay particles, and pores filled with air or water or both.

As a result, a relationship reflecting soil anisotropy (having properties that differ according to the direction of measurement) has been established between the structure of certain arbitrarily chosen soils and their mode of failure under load.

New Leads in Oil Research:

Drilling for oil and gas is an expensive operation and in the offshore sedimentary basins around Australia a typical well can cost between three and four million dollars . . .

Research by the Division of Mineral Chemistry on the formation of hydrocarbons in rocks should enable exploration companies to improve the success of their drilling operations. The Division has shown that chemical examination of coals and carbonaceous material encountered during drilling can be used to help identify potential source beds of petroleum and natural gas, to estimate the probable depth at which oil and gas might occur, and to predict whether a particular area is likely to yield oil and gas, gas condensate, or dry gas.

Filter Aids from Coal:

Filter aids are used in industry for such purposes as water purification, mineral dressing, effluent treatment, filtration of vegetable oils and petroleum products, and the clarification of beverages. A filter aid added to a liquid before filtering forms a porous layer on the filter which stops it from becoming blocked with sludge and removes fine particles that might otherwise leave the filtered liquid cloudy. The most widely used filter aid is diatomaceous earth which costs about $200 a ton . . .

A few years ago, the Division of Mineral Chemistry found that filter aids could be from coal produced by controlled carbonization in a fluidized bed. In many cases, the new materials were equal in performance to good grades of diatomaceous earth and had the advantage that after being used they could be disposed of by burning . . .

The process of manufacturing these filter aids and activated carbons is simple, and the Division expects the cost of production to be low . . .

Tests show that activated coal-based filter aids provide an excellent alternative to bone char in sugar refining and in the production of glucose . . . and for the recovery of solvent used in dry cleaning plants.

One of the biggest outlets for coal-based filter aids, however, may be in the aluminum industry, where they appear to have considerable promise for handling the red mud which is left behind when crude bauxite is purified by treatment with caustic soda.

Whiter Wool:

Bleached wool is particularly suitable for white or pastel fabrics and so commands premium prices. The usual commercial method of bleaching wool is to treat it with hydrogen peroxide, but wool treated in this way is much more sensitive to subsequent yellowing by the action of sunlight, alkalis, or heat.

In scouring mills, one of the traditional methods used for upgrading slightly yellow wool is to spread the wool on the top floor of a building under a glass roof and turn it occasionally with a fork to expose fresh material to the light. The glass roof filters out the low wavelength ultraviolet radiation which turns wool creamy yellow, but admits blue light, which has a bleaching effect. The treatment usually takes one to two days.

Experiments conducted by the Division of Protein Chemistry showed that a similar bleaching effect could be achieved in one or two hours by exposing wet wool to filtered blue lights from banks of mercury vapour lamps, but the improvement in the value of the wool barely offsets the cost of treatment.

However, following reports from overseas that certain reducing agents produced a bleaching effect, the Division found that treating wool with thoglycollic acid and exposing it to blue light resulted in much faster (5 to 10 minutes) and much better bleaching . . .

Recording Temperatures in Tanning Drums:

Tanning of hides to produce leather is usually carried out in rotating wooden drums. One of the factors influencing the quality of the leather is the temperature at which tanning is carried out, but until recently little was known about the variations in temperature that occur during the run . . .

The Division of Protein Chemistry has designed an instrument which can be attached to the drum and which transmits information on the temperature by means of an audio-frequency electromagnetic signal to a pick-up coil mounted nearby on a stationary part of the machine.

The signals can be taken by coaxial cable to a receiver and then to a chart recorder . . .

(And there were still some people in the latter half of the 20th Century who thought of Australia as an "undeveloped" country! Most of them were in the United States.)

Shrinkproofing of Wool:

In 1966, the Division of Textile Industry Physics announced the development of an improved method for shrinkproofing wool which involved applying a thin layer of resin to the surface of the wool fibres after treating them with a weak solution of chlorine.

This process is now being applied industrially in Australia and New Zealand and is about to be taken up by a number of other countries . . .

A scanning electron microscope acquired by the Division in 1968 has greatly simplified the task of assessing the uniformity and extent of resin application . . .

Transporting Beef in Containers:

In April 1969, Australia began shipping frozen boneless beef overseas in insulated containers . . . Each container had an overall size of 20 ft. by 8 ft. by 8 ft. and held 16 tons of beef packed in 60-lb. containers at well below freezing. It is then transported by road or rail to the nearest container terminal.

The Division of Food Preservation was asked to find out whether clip-on refrigeration units (to preserve the low temperatures in transit) would be needed for all containers during inland transport.

Several unrefrigerated trial runs by rail and road were made . . . and computer programs were set up to calculate heat flows into unrefrigerated containers. The results showed that clip-on refrigeration units were needed only on rare occasions, mainly for long journeys in midsummer.

Since the clip-on units cost up to $3500 each and added 1½ tons of non-payload per vehicle, this finding provided substantial savings to shippers of frozen beef. Similar studies were being made for lamb shipments.

Biscuits for the Undernourished:

The Division of Dairy Research has developed an attractive and nutritious milk biscuit containing all the essential ingredients of milk except lactose. The lactose is replaced with wheat flour and cane sugar to avoid undue browning . . .

The biscuits are a versatile food—they can be softened with water to serve as a food for weanlings or eaten dry as a snack for children or adults and serve as a supplement for diets in any section of a community with deficiencies of minerals or vitamins. The biscuits keep well and under tropical conditions last at least six months with adequate packing . . .

Several countries, including India, the territory of Papua and New Guinea, and Zambia have become interested in the biscuit . . .

Fire-resistant Fence Posts:

Round fence posts, properly treated with preservative against termites and decay, can last more than 30 years. Over one million posts are commercially treated in Australia each year, most of them with preservatives of the waterborne copper-chrome-arsenic (CCA) type and the number is growing steadily.

These preservatives have a number of advantages: they can be transported readily in concentrated form, they are simple to use, no heating is needed during processing, and both the preservative and posts treated with it are clean and easy to handle.

Posts treated with CCA do not catch fire readily and usually withstand the fire better than untreated hardwood posts, but once ignited they usually smolder until completely consumed. While this peculiar "after-glow" effect is the only disadvantage of the CCA treatment, it could seriously affect the future use of treated posts . . .

After experimenting with a number of preservatives, the Division of Forest Products has developed several formulations of the CCA type which eliminate the "after-glow" problem . . .

The new preservatives are expected to add only a few cents to the cost of each treated post.

(In a world that suffers tens of thousands of deaths by fire, and incalculable property losses from fires in wooden structures, wouldn't it be possible to examine the possibility that all wood used in new construction be given the same treatment as the fence posts?)

Diffraction Gratings:

Optical diffraction gratings commonly take the form of extremely flat metal-coated glass plates with large numbers of closely spaced grooves (up to 32,000 per inch) ruled on them. They are used in a variety of optical instruments to separate light into its component colours.

In high quality gratings, the grooves must be straight to within one-millionth of an inch and parallel to better than 0.1 second of arc, all grooves must be well within one-millionth of an inch of their correct position with respect to the first groove, and the grooves must be of the same shape, width and depth to within one millionth of an inch.

As a result of the work of the Division of Chemical Physics over the last ten years, Australia is now one of the few countries in the world where first quality diffraction gratings are produced commercially.

Mapping Bush Fires from the Air:

Keeping track of the course of bush fires and detecting new outbreaks is a major problem for anyone directing operations against fires in inaccessible country. Attempts to observe fires during the day from light aircraft have met with only limited success. The flames are often so obscured by smoke that accurate mapping of the fire edges is impossible.

An infrared detector developed a few years ago by the Division of Applied Chemistry enables aerial observers to view many flame fronts that would otherwise be invisible.

At night, an aerial observer can see fire edges and spot fires quite clearly through the thickest smoke, but he is then faced with the problem of trying to determine his exact position.

The Division has been able to solve this problem by using precision dead-reckoning navigation and a portable radio beacon located at a known position near the fire area. The aircraft flies known tracks from the beacon and fire edges are mapped as the observer passes over them.

More Efficient Power Generation:

Although modern large steam power stations operate at steam temperatures around 1050°F and pressures up to 3500 lb/in², only about 40 percent of the energy in the fuel is converted into electrical energy . . .

On the other hand, with gas turbine cycles the pressures are much lower but the efficiency is limited by the difficulty of recovering the low-grade heat from the turbine exhaust.

In an attempt to overcome these disadvantages, engineers have proposed combining the two cycles, using a carbonizer to provide a gaseous fuel for a gas turbine and burning the residual char with the turbine exhaust in a steam boiler . . .

The Division of Chemical Engineering has been examining the operational requirements for a 275 megawatt combined-cycle power station for Australian conditions. Using CSIRO's digital computer to investigate a mathematical model of such a station, the Division was able to study the performance of the station with respect to operating variables . . .

At different operating temperatures, cost reductions for the production of electrical energy would be reduced from 1.7 percent to 5 percent . . .

Refining Metals:

A common way of removing a dissolved impurity from a molten metal during refining is to add a reagent that will precipitate the impurity as an insoluble compound which can be removed as a slag or dross . . .

Metallurgists have been able to do this only after long and difficult experiments followed by expensive plant-scale trials . . .

Cloud Seeding by Pyrotechnics:

The Division of Radiophysics is trying a new method of cloud seeding in which silver iodide and a pyrotechnic mixture are loaded into cartridges and shot into the tops of clouds from an aircraft instead of being released into the bases as is usual.

The material in the cartridge weighs only about 7 ounces, but as it burns and falls through the cloud it produces high concentrations of active silver iodide nuclei . . .

Dramatic cloud growth and heavy rain have often followed this kind of seeding.

Radio Pictures of the Sun:

The radioheliograph operated by the Division of Radiophysics at the CSIRO Solar Observatory at Culgoora, New South Wales, is a unique instrument which gives a rapid sequence of detailed pictures of the sun in the "light" of radio waves . . .

These "radio pictures" are displayed on two picture tubes. One tube shows radiation that is circularly polarized in the left-handed sense, the other shows radiation that is circularly polarized in the right-handed sense . . .

Measuring High Pressures:

Very high fluid pressures can be measured accurately by observing their effect on the melting point of mercury . . . Established forms·of apparatus used to measure pressures of the order of 10,000 atmospheres are massive. Because of this, there is a delay of 20 minutes or more before temperature affects resulting from changes in the pressure of the working fluid diminish to the point where an accurate measurement can be made.

The Division of Physics has developed a technique for determining the melting point of mercury under pressure which involves only a small amount of mercury housed in polyethylene within a steel capillary tube. The onset of melting is observed by detecting the small amount of heat absorbed in the melting process.

With this technique, highly reproductable results can be obtained quickly . . .

Promoting Corrosion with an Inert Gas:

The gases helium, neon, argon, krypton, xenon, and radon are known as the inert gases because of their chemical inactivity. In recent years, however, it has been found that they can combine with fluorine. Xenon, for example, combines with fluorine to form xenon fluoride. The Division of Tribophysics has shown that the formation of xenon fluoride is catalyzed by a variety of metals, one of the most active being nickel . . .

Crystals That Don't Obey the Rules:

Early last century, John Dalton propounded his law of definite proportions which states that in every compound the constituent elements are always in the same proportions.

Towards the end of last century, however, a number of inorganic crystalline compounds were found which apparently did not obey this law.

Such compounds are said to be non-stoichiometric. Many of these compounds are of interest to metallurgists because minerals go through a nonstoichiometric stage during smelting. They also are of interest to solid-state physicists and chemists since nonstoichiometry leads to unusual electrical properties in semiconductors and also to useful optical properties in various materials.

For some years, it was thought that all nonstoichiometric compounds contained "holes" or vacant sites in their crystal lattice which should have been occupied by atoms but weren't.

Recently, the Division of Mineral Chemistry has shown that many nonstoichiometric compounds have a quite different basis . . .

Many of these materials have been examined by the Division of Tribophysics under the electron microscope . . . in this way the detailed structure of small crystals was determined . . .

Measuring Gravity:

The absolute measurement of force, pressure, and many other physical quantities requires a knowledge of the local value of g, the gravitational acceleration. Absolute determinations of g have been made at a few sites in North America and Europe. Instruments calibrated at these sites have been used elsewhere to obtain local values for g, but the local values obtained in this way do not have the same degree of accuracy.

For the last few years, the Division of Applied Physics has been working on an absolute determination of g.

Although the method used employs a number of novel techniques, it is simple in theory and consists essentially of timing the rise and fall of a body when it is thrown up. In practice, however, a number of technical difficulties have had to be overcome to achieve the desired accuracy. Although some possible sources of systematic error still have to be investigated, preliminary results indicate that the required accuracy of 1 in 10 million should be achieved.

Helping the Programmer:

Scientific research is always dealing with fresh problems and new computer programmes are continually being evolved to handle them. In CSIRO, probably as much computer time is spent on developing new programmes as on using these programmes to process data. To help programmers in the preparation, editing and testing of their new programmes, the Division of Computing Research has

East of Silverton lay the Mount Gipps
sheep station with stone homestead and
stone shearing shed and all the stores
and huts of a self-contained village. Not
far away was a grog shanty, where the
station hands could cash their cheques,
and a police station where the constable
could supervise their shanty. In a small
cemetery in the red sand, wooden
tablets marked the graves of swagmen
and station hands who had died of too
much alcohol or too little water. Glassy
pieces of quartz littered the ridges like
shining salt . . .

Scattered hills eased the monotony
of the undulating plains . . . in between
was a long low hill with jagged crest as
if the top of the hill had been broken.
They called it the Broken Hill . . .

GEOFFREY BLAINEY, The Rush That
Never Ended, Melbourne University
Press, 1963.

PRO HART

designed and implemented a monitor system . . .

The system incorporates six keyboard display consoles located in the Division's computing laboratory in Canberra. The consoles provide programmers with direct access to the central processor so that they can check and test their programmes during the course of the operation . . .

Recently, the system has been extended by the addition of five teleprinters . . .

The teleprinters are on-line to a small computer that is connected to the main computer by an interface designed and constructed as a Divisional research project . . .

Saving Time on Computers:

Each day the Division of Computing Research processes over one thousand jobs on its computer in Canberra. Most of these jobs are short—usually less than one minute.

Before a programme can be run, however, it must be translated into a language that can be understood by the particular computer being used and it also must be loaded into the computer. These two steps can take longer than the time taken to run a programme so that a significant fraction of the time of short jobs and of total available computing time is used up in this unproductive manner.

By modifying the translation programme supplied by the manufacturer, and by implementing a new loading technique that uses the random access storage available in magnetic drums, the Division has been able to speed up the translation of programmes by about five times and to free the computer for several hours more computing time each day. The Division has

named this new system KWIKTRAN.

One was tempted to catch the next KWIKTRAN if one could, because it had been a long watch and one was suffering a little from eyeball cramp and the 20th Century blues.

But one felt the time had not been wasted, for one appeared to have discovered something important here—an already established and competently operating scientific research organization capable of performing on a global scale.

As an institution, it was well funded, well staffed, well directed; an interdisciplinary institution that could perform its seemingly modest but really extraordinary service to the world of man upon his planetary stage.

CSIRO did not walk alone.

There was another vast creature roaming about, snuffling along its own trails, tracking the future—as much as the CSIRO.

In the now slowly dimming light of a century not yet born one could discern some log entries labeled "Department of National Development," which was more popularly labeled Nat/Dev, or, when time was short, just N/D.

This creature described itself as (gulp) "the principal Commonwealth department with responsibility for the formulation of policy concerning the assessment and development of Australia's natural resources" particularly in the fields of minerals, water, forests and energy.

A little later, entries in the log became harder to follow. The crew of the Raft had changed their political masters at the ballot-box. The new masters tossed Nat/Dev overboard and re-assigned its duties amongst the Department of Minerals and Energy, the Department of Northern Development and the Department of Primary Industry.

There was every chance that after subsequent ballot-box changes the old organization would be revived but the work that Nat/Dev had been involved in was still being done: the geodetic survey and topographic mapping of Australia; bathymetric survey of the continental shelf; co-ordination of development in Northern Australia; field stations involved in aspects of geology, geophysics or forestry in Western Australia, South Australia, Tasmania, Victoria, Queensland, Northern Territory and Papua-New Guinea.

Through Ministers, Nat/Dev or the other departments had links with the Australian Atomic Energy Commission, the Joint Coal Board, the Snowy Mountains Hydro-Electric Authority. Links with the State Governments were maintained through the Australian Forestry Council, the Australian Water Resources Council and the Australian Minerals Council.

So although Nat/Dev looked like a CSIRO (or would have looked like one if you put the parts back together again) it was not a CSIRO. It marched to a different drum.

One flipped a page and found under "Water Research" that it had great gulpability:

Study of the hydrology of small rural catchments . . . Research requirements in urban hydrology and design of urban storm water disposal systems . . . Application of models to stream flow measurements . . . A field study of evaporation, and an investigation into evaporation reduction on water storages . . . Problems of developing underground water supplies in river valleys . . . The conjunctive use of surface and groundwater resources . . . Artificial groundwater recharge study . . . Study of salinity problems to determine whether factors such as clearing for agriculture will affect water supplies . . . Identification of the nature and mechanism of the corrosion of pre-stressed reinforcement wire in concrete water structures and the corrosion of groundwater pumping equipment.

Flip another page; skip the River Murray Commission and the Snowy Mountains Scheme, give a brief nod to Nuclear Energy and settle on International:

A number of technical papers and briefing papers on water and energy matters associated with Australia's interests in United Nations were prepared . . . These were particularly concerned with the Economic Commission for Asia and the Far

East (E.C.A.F.E.), United Nations Educational, Scientific and Cultural Organization (U.N.E.S.C.O.), World Meteorological Organization (W.M.O.), and the International Atomic Energy Association (I.A.E.A.).

Dreary as this recitation might appear, it did serve to establish that Nat/Dev *was* an international operation with high capabilities; that its borders were not the edges of the Australian continent, nor even The Reef, but extended throughout the world.

A primary function of the Nat/Dev Bureau of Mineral Resources, Geology and Geophysics was to obtain, study and provide basic geological, geophysical and economic information necessary for the exploration and development of the nation's mineral resources.

Field operations included:

Carpentaria Basins: Part of the Carpentaria Basin was mapped jointly by the Bureau and the Geological Survey of Queensland in 1969 and 1970 . . .

Great Artesian Basin: Surface mapping of the Great Artesian Basin in Queensland was completed in 1970-71. Because of rather meagre outcrops, geological and geophysical surveys were supplemented by a programme in which water bores throughout the basin were logged to determine physical characteristics and to deduce the geology of the rocks penetrated.

Broad Sound Estuary: A detailed survey of modern estuaries was begun—its purpose to examine factors that determine the deposition and concentration of minerals in estuarine environments.

Considering how much of the world's population is clustered around what are primarily estuarine areas (i.e., "an arm of the sea that extends inland to meet a river") this seemingly local research could easily have global implications.

And there were many more, perhaps too many to try to cover in the brief watch. One picked a couple at random, just to show what was going on:

South Australian Gravity Survey: A helicopter gravity survey using a regular grid of reconnaissance gravity stations completed the coverage of the state . . .

Meekatharra Aeromagnetic Survey: An aeromagnetic survey of the Kingston, Wiluna, and Glengarry areas . . . was carried out to provide regional aeromagnetic coverage of the Precambrian Shield in Western Australia.

Precambrian, anyone?

Much of the world, that's who.

Marine Geophysical Survey: An area including the Bismarck Sea, the coastal waters off southeast Papua and in the Gulf of Carpentaria Basin were surveyed by continuous seismic reflection, gravity and magnetic methods. The problems of very accurate position and speed measurements were largely solved by satellite doppler and VLF (very low frequency) techniques. Three computers were used on board.

Another way of finding out about the land from the air was tried in the:

New Guinea Airborne Seismic Survey. The Bureau attempted what is believed to have been the world's first experimental airborne survey aimed at establishing a practicable method of application of seismic surveys to areas inaccessible for conventional land seismic operations.

A helicopter was used to position explosives, shooting equipment and sonobuoy transmitters, signals from which were received in a conventional recording system mounted on an aircraft.

Oh my word, how much more of this does one have to bear? Quite a bit; but what is being established here is extraordinary scientific and technological competence.

In paleontology, a fauna collected at Bullock Creek, Northern Territory, in 1969 has been examined . . .

The Pliocene marsupial *Protemnodon otibandus* Plane, first described from New Guinea, was identified in a marine sequence from Victoria and from Chinchilla, Queensland. It is, therefore, the widest ranging kangaroo yet known.

As one scanned the faded log entries entitled Nat/Dev one found an amazing diversity of competency. Here are some:

Indigenous crude oil . . . natural gas . . . liquefied petroleum gas . . . coal research . . . petrology, geochemistry and geochronology . . . petroleum technology . . . sedimentology . . . photogeology . . . geobiological research . . . ionospheric recording . . . geomagnetics . . . seismology . . . geophysics . . . vulcanologics . . . silviculture sections with subsections of botany, genetics, seeds and soils . . . protection section with subsections of entomology, fire control, pathology and watershed management . . . forest inventory and mensuration . . . biometrics.

The "ologies" marched like a phalanx of Macedonian troops down the paths of the observable world.

This formidable army of scientists and technicians marching into the future was not without its humour—albeit unintended.

Like this entry:

"Water Bombing of Forest Fires: Preliminary investigations into water bombing of forest fires showed that the use of amphibious aircraft which scoop water directly from the lakes would be impractical in Australia because of the scarcity of suitable areas of fresh water . . ."

Seems to figure, doesn't it? Those would be mighty rough landings for amphibious planes scooping up water from a dry lake.

After a brief, but polite laugh, the phalanx marched inexorably and confidently toward the 21st Century, almost arrogant in its confidence. And with every right to be.

In a sense, Nat/Dev appeared to be a scanning mechanism; it had already mapped more of Australia, New Guinea and Antarctica than any other country had mapped of its own territory.

In the corner of its map's-eye, it saw that other scanning creature there—with its multifaceted eye fixed firmly on the measurable universe.

One could ask whether these two great systems could not get together and produce between them not only a laboratory for the world in science and technology, but something totally new—a laboratory for social and economic, psychological and political research of global dimensions.

At the present stage of man's world, there was still need for scientific and technological exploration, but there already appeared to be more science and technology than this poor old planet could digest.

Now it appeared to be time for some kind of institutional exploration that would serve as an enzyme, or catalyst, or something to help the people of the world to adapt to and assimilate these extraordinary inputs. This research could take place, of course, under "laboratory" conditions. Here was "world enough and time" in the Australiana complex.

Suppose, just suppose, that their charters (from the Commonwealth government) could be amended so that each organization could expand its services into the social and economic fields. These would be longterm 20 to 30 year studies, paid for by those countries throughout the world which had no space for large scale human experiments.

What might some of these Australian-monitored experiments be?

One could think of a few.

Population Density Studies:

One still did not know, in any scientific way, what the psychological, social and economic effects of high density occupation of humans in limited space areas could be. Some studies on rats seemed to indicate that there was a point at which the density reached the "critical point" (much as in nuclear fission) and the result was tension, anxiety and ultimately a paranoid culture. One knew this about rats, but one did not know this about humans. With the world population increasing at an exponential rate, with the continued migration from rural areas to urban centers, it seemed high time to find out.

The application of contemporary technology, including modular living space units, soundproofing, electronic communications (TV, radio, phonographs, etc.) might show that very high densities could be achieved without causing the problems the rats had.

The human "space bubble" was a rather small one; it seemed to require only privacy, reasonable comfort, and continuous contact with the world outside. All of these were well within the range of contemporary technology, but how these things could realistically be put together, and on what scale of density, was still not known.

Traffic and Transportation Control:

Related to population density was the problem of traffic and transportation control. The movement of people, goods and services in areas of high population density was one of the great unsolved problems of the latter part of the 20th Century.

Yet if people, goods and services were considered as "bits" of information, then it was possible that the application of communications theory, coupled with the application of general systems theory and transactional analysis, could be relevant to solving these problems under controlled conditions.

It certainly seemed that Australia had the computer resources and the scientific and technological expertise to take that one on.

High-Rise or Horizontal Construction:

Well now, one could go up or down, or sidewise in the planned construction of a human habitat. But nobody seemed to know which way to go. Perhaps the question was improperly asked. It might instead be, what combination of these modes would be most productive for increasing the value of human life, preservation of the ecology, and as a means of meeting the towering waves of change that will sweep over the community?

But nobody knew. This would have to be an interdisciplinary approach, and it would take space, time and patience. Australia had those.

How to Design a City:

One pondered the advantages and disadvantages of "spiral configurations" or the more conventional "grid systems" of urban design and one did not have too much information to go wondering about. Or was there some other topographical configuration that hadn't even been described by the topologists yet?

Australia had had one experience with a wholly planned city—Canberra. After a rather slow getting used to, it finally caught on and turned out to be a perfectly beautiful place. It was of circular design, with vast sheets of green lawns and trees, monuments that glowed like alabaster at the end of great tree-lined avenues, luminescent in the man-dawn of evening.

It was akin to the original plan in Washington, D.C., as well as the yet-to-be achieved plan for Tokyo in the year 2000.

At Canberra, man-made Lake Burley Griffin gurgled and spouted like some enormous sea creature.

If the Australians could build such a city for the sceptre-carrying members of Parliament, could they not also help design and build one for other countries? Under contract and for a fee, of course.

Cottage Industry vs. Centralized Ones:

Given the accelerated spread of the thin "electronic film" in the post-industrial age it was at least possible that the centralization of industries and services could be eliminated and replaced with what could amount to space age "cottage industry." The advantages could be a reduction in environmental destruction, in pollution, considerable savings in commuting costs, a relaxation of tension and the possibility of a greatly increased pride in the quality of the goods or services produced as compared to the rigid and repetitive modes of mass-production societies.

THE WORLD OF DREAMS

I

Thou hast thy world of dreams
Where veiled and hidden from thyself
thou walkest as in sleep.
In that enchanted place the real is
what seems,
And that which seems enfolds thee
in its keep.
Yet shall there come a day when thou
must wake,
When, rent, the fabric of thy world
shall break,
Then shalt thou feel thy senses stir
in shock
Like the young sheep-dog scenting
first the flock.
In that far day tread softly, O my sweet,
Lest the dreams pierce thy feet.

MARY GILMORE: Selected Verse,
Mary Gilmore, Angus & Robertson,
Ltd., Sydney, 1948.

Desmond Norman
Mrs. Bates and Gin-Di-Gi

There was plenty of room and plenty of technology for some experiments in "cottage industry" in Australia. All that was needed was the will to give some people a chance and, of course, to figure out the distribution problems, which could be formidable.

Mixed Ethnic Communities:

It had not so far been determined how mixed races and ethnic groups could be assimilated peacefully in urban environments with high population densities. One knew what had happened in uncontrolled urban environments—uncontrolled in the sense that they just sort of happened.

But things could be different now. The opportunities for cultural, racial, linguistic and ideological intercommunication were greater than they have ever been.

Wouldn't somebody—like the Israelis and the Arabs—like the Catholics and the Protestants in Ireland—like the blacks and whites of South Africa—like to try out ways of accommodation away from local pressures and prejudices?

Towards more manly wethers

Treating healthy wethers with the male hormone testosterone slightly increases wool and meat production. An operation that makes male lambs 'cryptorchid' probably does this also. Both testosterone-treated wethers and cryptorchids produce leaner meat than normal wethers.

Dung beetles on the move

CSIRO winning war against fly scourge

The days may be numbered for probably Australia's greatest pest — the fly.

Flies, Spiders and Toads

One could start with flies. If there was one thing Australia had more of than it needed, it was flies. Particularly up north, where the hot breath of the tropic winds fans them into incredible swarms. If one were a mad dog or Englishman and went out in the midday sun—the flies would follow as the night the day.

Now these are not the nice little houseflies that so delight the hearts of Americans and Europeans. These are bush flies and buffalo flies big enough to drive a full grown steer into distraction and a whole herd of cattle into panic. They have a proboscis as big as a dentist's drill and use it much more wantonly. So, our first character enters, several million years too soon.

The European colonizers introduced cattle to a land that had accommodated to marsupials. The cattle, like any other living beings, took in food at one end and deposited what it did not need at the other. Tubes, even as you and I.

What was deposited at the other end was rich in nutrients, warm and moist, and a perfect place for flies to deposit their eggs. As the number of cattle increased, so did the flies.

Since 1967 the CSIRO Division of Entomology has been releasing dung beetles in northern Australia, and several species have become well established. One, *Onthophagus gazella*, has spread spectacularly, and already it has apparently begun to control that menace to cattlemen in the north—the buffalo fly. The beetles should improve soil fertility too. The Division has now begun liberating new species in the southern half of the continent that should help to reduce the bushfly nuisance.

Bushflies retreat?

The equation was a pretty simple one; the more cattle, the more flies—at an exponential rate. For the flies.

So, what to do?

A Dr. G. F. Bornemissza of the CSIRO Division of Entomology came up with an idea in 1960 and in 1963, his proposal was put into effect.

Like all good ideas, it was a quite simple one.

Dr. Bornemissza pointed out that in most of the warmer countries of the world, dung beetles carry out the task of clearing away the droppings of native animals. They do this by burying the droppings in the ground while still fresh as food for themselves and their offspring.

"Here in Australia, indigenous beetles do the same with pellet-like droppings of the native marsupials, but they cannot cope with the large wet dung pats of domestic stock introduced by European man.

"Cattle and their close relatives evolved beetles that use their dung. The programme involves introducing the best of the beetles into Australia . . ."

What would these little creatures do?

According to the CSIRO predictions, they would:
• free pastures from dung accumulation
• fertilize the soil
• control pests

Cow pats often last for months or even years in Australia, so they cover considerable areas of ground and prevent pasture growth. Termites have a major effect in removing dung, but they take months to do so. Australia's 20 million odd cattle each produce about 10 pats a day, so many hundreds of acres of pasture must be lost annually for this reason. Dung beetles could prevent this loss.

As everyone knows, most Australian soils lack fertility. Fresh dung contains nitrogen, which is lost into the atmosphere when the dung lies on the surface of the ground . . . By burying the droppings of stock, dung beetles could considerably increase fertility. They could also do some other housekeeping chores as well.

Insects lay their eggs in the fresh droppings. If the droppings are buried quickly enough, the larvae cannot develop.

There were other pests, too, which could affect livestock who also used the pats as incubators, and the same treatment got rid of them, too.

So selected beetle species from Africa and Asia, which had previously been successfully introduced into Hawaii (to control horn beetles) were given Australian citizenship. Some 275,000 of them were spotted about in tropical Australia and they very quickly went to work. There was plenty of work to do.

It worked fine, and a particular species of beetle, *Onthophagus gazella*, proved a star of the performance. Since the first experiments, a number of other species of beetles have been investigated and some of them implanted.

But like all good plans of mice and men, something "went agley."

Turned out there were native species of small poisonous spiders that delighted in eating dung beetle larvae. So pretty soon the whole place was infested with spiders; in the stock area one sat down gingerly, if at all.

So, the second major character had entered the act. As far as humans were concerned trading flies for poisonous spiders was not a very good deal.

But there was relief in sight. Enter from left stage, a species of toad that relished spiders. Good. Reduced the fly population. Now reduced the spiders. Only trouble now was too many toads.

What to do now? Introduce hawks to eat the toads who ate the spiders who ate the dung beetle larvae? Just like the house that Jack built.

It remained to be seen how many hawks one wanted around, so it might be necessary to introduce some other species—like eagles, for instance—to control the hawks.

What would control the over-abundance of eagles was not immediately clear.

But one could bet the Australians would solve the problem.

They were that kind of people.

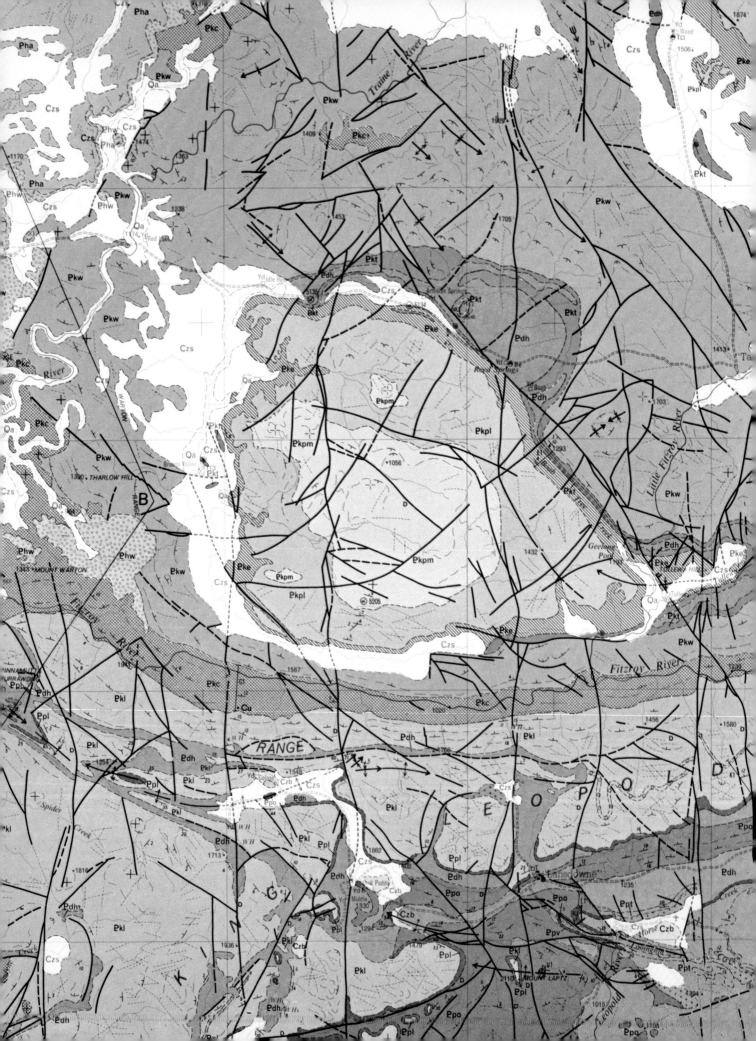

Like all the ships that sailed the ocean sea, the Stone Raft carried a scientist or two. One remembered, Darwin on the "Beagle" and many others.

Long after ship, captain and crew had disappeared, what these supercargoes saw and felt and wrote about remains. They somehow had the wondrous curiosity of children. And in hours of the night they wrote the wonder of the world.

The land there—a vast spectrum of environments—a mirror image of all the rest of the world: fire and ice, sun and rain, mountains and deserts, islands and reefs. The scientific and technological talent was there—much of it attracted from Europe and the United States by the magnetism of the Stone Raft. The time was there—perhaps all the time that human civilization had left.

The question that remained to be answered was whether there was the organizational and managerial ability to form and manage a "Laboratory for the World."

One thought so.

At least it seemed there might be—foreshadowed in the twin organizations of the Commonwealth Science and Industrial Organization and the Department of National Development. These two projections of human aspiration were as alike as twin brothers; but each to each, as different also. Contemplating them, one saw that widespread, longterm and highly sophisticated scientific and technological programs could be initiated, organized and carried out.

There also appeared to be a basic honesty in both organizations—a commodity in rather short supply at the present. Neither succumbed to expediency for political or economic reasons. Well, perhaps that had happened once in awhile, but for the most part they were trying to find out what was going on, even if the trail they were following petered out in the frustration of the grand outback of the human experience.

The two organizations operated in a highly pragmatic society that was honed sharp by the challenge of a strange land. They depended on results, not on gaudy press releases made up from the fantasies of persons who had never burned a tick out of their leg with a cigarette, nor spent weeks studying a tidal pool, or patiently counted the flies from a pile of dung.

So, one felt there was a solid substructure there—honesty and curiosity bred of the continent itself; a government more permissive than most, and a general public that was willing to wait for results; most of it was going to be spending a day at the races anyway.

But to the people who had the administrative responsibilities for guiding these organizations, the problems were not easily solved, not even on the national level—much less on a potential international one.

A basic question was why "ordinary" people should be willing to pay for something most of them could not even understand.

It is almost certainly the case that simply by promoting science other nonscientific ends will sooner or later benefit to a considerable extent. So that over the long period expenditure on science will still be justifiable in its instrumental role . . . There is a surprising amount of agreement between those economists and scientists who have written on this matter, that current decisions should be taken on the view that science is a means and not an end . . .
In very broad terms governments are concerned to promote the flow of new knowledge and to ensure that existing science and technology is successfully applied.
—LEON PERES: "Organizing Science as a Means," *Public Administration*, December, 1965 (Canberra)

There was a certain hazard here—that the value of pure scientific research might be limited to purely utilitarian ends. Such an approach would, indeed, be putting the cart before the horse; useful going downhill, the cart could pull the horse, but not very easy climbing a steep grade.

Theoretically, at least, pure scientific research is concerned primarily with the relationships between the human neural system and the environmental systems in which it is immersed; from stars to atoms, from whales to microbes, from fungus to fir trees.

Such decisions were necessarily future-oriented because they were without precedent. They were also preemptive, in that if the research funds were allocated to one field of research, it was denied another. These choices were inevitably intuitive; no previous experience was available. The directors, allocators, distributors, or whatever one wanted to call them, quite literally flew by the seats of their pants.

Even when a problem of great practical significance is known to exist it is clearly unwise to embark on extensive research activities unless the scientists can see the possibility of an original discovery from which a solution might flow. Conversely, it is frequently true that scientific discovery itself may provide unsuspected and novel opportunities for economic development. Discoveries emerge from imaginative thinking; the role of the individual scientists is vital . . .
—LEON PERES: "Organizing Science as a Means," *Public Administration*, December, 1965 (Canberra)

Dr. Peres goes on to explain in considerable detail the two horns of the administrative dilemma; "centralization or decentralization?" Those were big words, but can be reduced to a somewhat simpler question: "Who knows most about the problem, the guy out there on his hands and knees watching an ant, or his 'boss' sitting in an air-conditioned office, fluorescent-lighted, reading a copy of *The Financial Times?*"

Rather obviously, it would take both. The man in the field knew what the ant was doing; the man in the office knew where the money might come from to pay for the man to sit there watching the ant.

There was something out there now. Something not quite seen. It was lurking on the outskirts of the mind. What was it?

There it was! Almost scurrying out of sight. Not quite.

Suppose it was that the Australian had an extraordinary talent for turning theory into practical application?

Somehow, the dreams of the theorists emerged from the groves of academe—they bounded and hopped, fluttered and flew, slithered and swam, crawled and crept—into something rich and new.

Perhaps the harsh environment itself dictated that words were not enough; perhaps it was a particularly Australian grain of mind. Whatever, it worked for the bloated cattle, the tick-ridden steers, the termites, wood chips and so many other things. They were worth looking at, these strange projections of the dawn, and these apparitions of Dreamtime.

One scanned them with a somewhat incredulous wonder; the notes of night, and the tones of dawn.

Here were some:

A near classic example of the marriage of theory and technical application was that concerning cattle bloat.

To the city-sider, cattle bloat would not seem much of a problem, but to the cattle raiser, it was.

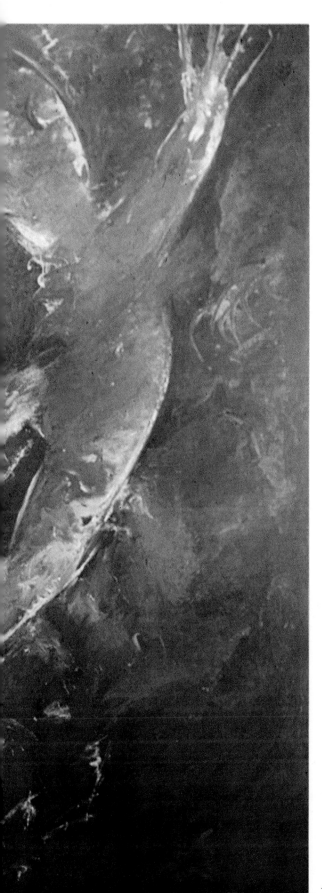

The good thing about great paintings is that one can read anything one likes into them. Perhaps one could read in Arthur Boyd's painting that "Australia Fair" is attacking the evils (the "Beast) that beset the world.

It should be noted that the girl is red-haired (like the red soils that cover so much of Australia) that she is vibrant and aggressive like the Australians themselves, and that "the Beast" is a weak and pallid creature.

One cannot help but believe that "Australia Fair" will triumph in the end. It's a fair go!

A. Boyd
NUDE WITH BEAST

Now, bloat is caused by the cow eating too much green fodder, or drinking too much water, or both. What happens is that bubbles are formed in the rumen, and the cow "bloats."

The way to stop this from happening is to use detergents; little bubbles break up the big bubbles.

Bloat control has one feature in common with dishwashing —the need to maintain an adequate concentration of detergent . . .
Dosing a cow with detergent immediately establishes a high concentration in the rumen, which falls steeply as the rumen contents are replaced with freshly eaten food, water and saliva . . .
—*Rural Research*, CSIRO December, 1972

So, what does one do? One way would be to invent and develop a capsule which the cow would swallow. The capsule would come to rest in the rumen; there it would release detergent over a period of many weeks. The capsule was designed so that when the detergent was used up, the capsule split apart and the cow could throw it up. Now that all may seem pretty simple, but it really wasn't:

Occasionally, instead of swallowing the capsule, certain animals propel it back up and spit it at the operator's feet . . . All ruminants can regurgitate objects from their stomachs, since they do so whenever they ruminate. However, most cattle swallow the capsule obediently perhaps to avoid seeing the disappointed look on the operator's face when a capsule falls at his feet.

It gave one something to ruminate on, did it not?

Sometimes it does not pay to be a cow. Another capsule coming. This one also goes into the rumen. The intelligent cow might say, "Mate, there's no more rumen there." But if one was intelligent, one wouldn't be a cow to begin with, would one?

This little story started like this:

Picture an improved winter pasture of short green grass and very little clover —a far cry from the lush, clover-filled paddocks of spring bloat. Cattle and their calves are standing unhappily with their backs to a cold July wind. The farmer . . . decides to move them to a sheltered paddock and sends in the dogs. To his alarm, the cattle react violently . . . Suddenly, one beast falls, convulsing. By the time the veterinarian arrives, six or seven of the older cattle are down, but an injection of magnesium salts restores all but one of them.
The farmer was lucky —he could have lost all the affected cattle. His pasture was a grass-tetany risk, deficient in magnesium.
—*Rural Research*, CSIRO December, 1972

But the good doctor had come up with a capsule. It was made up of two hollow, boat-shaped half-cylinders of magnesium . . . Release occurred by electrolysis and depended on the presence of a steel-wool cathode in each half, electrically connected to the magnesium cathode in each half. The acidic rumen contents formed the electrolyte, for what was in effect an electrical cell capable of producing 30 milliwatts of 1.0 volt.

So, here was a poor old cow, meandering around with a rumen full of capsules and wondering what, except jumping over the moon, in the world was coming next.

But the point, for humans at least, was that, faced with a practical problem, the Australians figured out a quite ingenious and exotic way to solve it. It involved physics and chemistry, metallurgy and animal husbandry.

This was not a mean achievement; there were a lot of cattle in the world whose rumen needed capsules. Perhaps the Australians could help.

One of the biggest hazards of commercial aircraft is birds on the flight path during takeoff and landing. Jets are particularly vulnerable, since the birds are sucked into the engine and reduce its performance at critical moments.

So, like virtually everything else, the Australians decided to look into this one, too. Mostly they were concerned about the Sydney airport, and at Townsville. At the latter, flocks of 30,000 brolgas have massed around the landing field during flight time.

How to keep the birds away?

Some safety standards already have been set up:

Present international air standards demand that an aircraft must be able to withstand striking a 4 lb. chicken at 400 knots. Moves are afoot to double this unusual measure to an 8 lb. turkey at 800 knots.
—*Rural Research*, CSIRO December, 1972

Now these regulations applied to the aircraft, but it is rather doubtful that the birds ever read them.

Back to the birds. Why do they flock around airports to begin with? One

Biological control of skeleton-weed

Three enemies of the weed, found after an intensive search throughout Mediterranean Europe, have established themselves in south-eastern Australia. The most promising — a rust fungus — took only 9 months to spread 100 miles from its release site near Wagga.

Keeping airfields bird-free

Bloat capsules, gel rings

A long-acting capsule in the rumen slowly releases detergent and controls bloat. It prevents death, allows better use of nutritious, legume-rich pastures, and boosts weight gain by beef cattle. Simpler and cheaper bloat preventives are also being tested.

reason is food, mostly in the sense of insects which cluster on the white landing lights required by international law. Strangely enough, yellow runway lights do not. So, changing back to the yellow lights might not be a bad idea.

Other less obvious circumstances may make airports attractive to the birds. For instance, mirages may attract pond insects that birds feed on. Again, shiny runways on wet nights often fool migrating waterfowl, which land on them. The unfortunate grebe cannot take off again without water.
—*Rural Research,* CSIRO December, 1972

Strangely enough, one of the most effective deterrents has proven to be falcons. But a jet running into a falcon is not much better off than when striking a flight of starlings or a five-pound turkey.

Better just change those runway lights; yellow was prettier anyway.

Two things important about this. The Australians were willing to spend the money and talent to find out. Second, many airports throughout the world are similarly plagued by birds, and perhaps the Australians can provide at least a partial answer.

It's all for the birds, anyway.

One had to take into account that what one firmly believed in was probably wrong. It was a hard lesson to learn, but once learned, usually late in life, it was a very valuable tool.

As a for instance, take the matter of watershed, land use and water tables. One had thought, for instance, that getting rid of stands of trees would mean faster runoff of rainwater and, therefore, less conservation of underground water during dry seasons.

Some South Australian scientists decided to look into it.

To their surprise, and perhaps to the surprise of many others in climatically similar regions throughout the world, they found it simply wasn't so.

A ten year study appeared to show that the evaporation from radiata pine stands was much greater than the collecting and holding of water by clear pastures. (The rainwater percolated down to aquifers and thus was still available through wells during the long, dry seasons.)

What one would expect is that wells would be drilled and the level of the water from time to time would be measured. And, of course, that was done.

In what was now appearing as a typical Australian style—living with the old while using the absolutely new—a new measurement was undertaken. It had almost the air of elegance about it.

. . . an ingenious technique that used fallout from nuclear tests to advantage. Tritium—the radioactive form of hydrogen—was one of the fallout products from the nuclear tests carried out in the northern hemisphere between 1954 and 1963 by the Americans, Russians and British. Once released into the upper atmosphere it started to fall to earth dissolved in the rain . . .
On infiltrating into the soil, tritium decays and so the concentration found in groundwater depends on how long ago it fell as rain, and its level in rainwater when it entered the soil. Measuring its concentration under forest and pasture can thus allow an estimate of the recharge rate.
—*Rural Research,* CSIRO December, 1972

So, that's what they did, and it turned out that the recharge under the forest was about one-sixth of that under pasture.

This may seem like a small thing, but it was not. In many areas of the world, devastated by forest fires, the replanting of trees is considered necessary to preserve the watershed. The Australian experiments would appear to show that replacement of the surface as pasture would conserve six times more ground-water than replanting the forest. There's always some grain of truth among the chaff.

The Wafted Seed

In parts of Australia, because there were few, if any, access roads suitable for heavy equipment, it was more practical to sow grass and clover seeds (for pasture lands) from low-flying planes.

Rather obviously, these seeds landed on top of the ground. If the ground was wet, it made for a happy landing. But in most of the places where aerial seeding was necessary, it was not wet. Often hard as stone.

The little air-dropped seed had a couple of problems. One of them was conserving moisture; the other was digging a foot down through the hard topsoil so it could reach the moisture beneath.

What could be done to help this little creature? Well, for one thing, it could be given a little coat that would absorb any moisture that might be in the vicinity. One little coat that performed well was a mixture of lime or bentonite and an adhesive called Methocel.

The way it turned out, the seeds with their little overcoats absorbed as much

as 135 percent of their dry weight while the little coatless ones took up only 40 percent dry weight.

Having grounded safely, the little seed needed some help because its protective coating would only last a little while. Another airlift took place, this time dropping straw cover to protect the seedling. For certain types of grass (rye grasses) the germination could be raised from about 12% to about 98%. Not bad, not bad.

The next mission was to spray herbicides over the area to cut down on competitors. Or maybe that preceded the aerial seeding. Anyway, it was a necessary step.

There was no way to help the seed drop its foot through the hard soil except to find ancestors that could. And these were found and various strains developed that could kick their way into existence.

It was not easy to grow a blade of grass in Australia, but it was done.

Try a little tenderness!

Some people—certainly the Americans —like their beef tender. In some areas or circles, or whatever one chooses to call them, a very tender beef steak or roast is considered a mark of quality.

Tenderness—as in human relations—is not easily achieved.

In beef (and perhaps with humans) it can depend on a number of variables. These include species, breed and age of

177

the animal, conditions and handling before and after slaughter, the particular muscle or "cut," and the method of cutting the meat.

Says *Rural Research:* "It is seldom possible to judge the eating qualities of meat by looking at it—you have to cook and taste it."

For quite a long time, it has been felt that "hanging meat" improved its flavor and tenderness. Perhaps this came out of earlier experience with wild game—such as deer and ducks. In the absence of suitable refrigeration facilities, one let the bacteria do the work and break down the connective tissues in the carcass.

No one really examined the theory; it was an ingrained response to a dead animal.

But was it really true? Some Australians decided to find out. The myth was only a myth:

Meat taken from a freshly killed animal and cooked quickly should be very tender. As rigor mortis develops, the muscles contract and the meat becomes steadily less tender, reaching a minimum when rigor mortis is fully developed.
—*Rural Research,* CSIRO September, 1972

Australians had always liked their meat "chewy," but that would not serve for the export market. How make it tender?

Well, one went into the production of lactic acid from glycogen, and hence the level of stored glycogen, and from there by rather devious paths to discover that glycogen levels determined meat quality. It was all a sort of Dr. Cloac and Mr. Hide adventure carried out in cold rooms and chill boxes, and far too complicated to detail here.

Anyway, this is what they found. If the carcass is hung in a different way, tenderness is increased—that is, a different way than has been traditional for several centuries. Instead of hanging the carcasses by the feet, it was possible to hang them another way.

As muscles go into rigor mortis they usually contract and become tougher. By hanging the carcass in a special way, its own weight positions the skeleton so that it stretches the muscles in a special way, thus reducing contraction and making meat more tender.
—*Rural Research,* CSIRO September, 1972

What seemed to be important about this was not so much that your beef and other meats might be more tender—but that a very simple way had been found to make it so without aging, without chemicals.

This meant that meat could be moved to market much more quickly and therefore more economically.

All they did was hang the carcass from the pelvis instead of from the Achilles heel. The process is called

178

"tenderstretch," which sounds like some kind of lingerie but only means that there are other ways of doing things.

And some of them are better.

Mystery of the White Ant

Not everyone sat around contemplating termites, but in many parts of Australia if one wanted to grow a crop, keep a roof over one's head, or even just keep a landing strip on an airfield open, one contemplated termites.

They were not "ants" at all, of course; they were their own species and they were abundant throughout the tropical and temperate regions. There was said to be some 95 different species throughout the world, and they ate different things, like houses, and furniture, forests, bushes, fences, animal fodder, anything.

Ernestine Hill in "The Territory" had recorded:

"One of the least of God's creatures, blind, defenseless, insensible, was eating their Australian hopes and their homes to a hollow shell."

White ants . . .

White ants ate the Residency piano, the mails in the postoffice, the pegs of miners' claims, wagon wheels while they were standing, blankets of sleepers in the night. They chewed jagged holes in the walls of the courthouse (in Darwin) and the police station, digested Government records, broke up the jail. . .

One of the Darwin dandies complained that white ants devoured his duelling pistols and his opera hat. . . They regaled themselves on billiard balls leaving a hollow globe of paint, then bored through sheets of lead to set the veranda posts aslant. They ate out the strongroom of the bank and while the manager was building a new one, they came up in thousands through the wet cement and twiddled their antennae at him in derision.

A mining director, absent for three months, came back to his home, put his key in the door, and the whole house fell flat.

Now, while Ernestine was of a romantic way of mind and a poetic turn of phrase, there seemed to be no doubt that the white ants did all these things, and are still doing them. In some parts of Australia, the ant hills were 25 feet high, dotted over hundreds of square miles.

For the white European settler, railroad builders, telephone pole erectors, construction men—almost anybody who worked with wood—the termite was a fierce and unconquerable enemy.

But perhaps that attitude might be changing, not because the termite, trapped in the amber of his genetic social organization, had changed for millions of years, but because man had.

Studies since 1965 by the scientists of the Division of Entomology (CSIRO) have been focused on the contributions termites may make to the natural ecology.

Termites do not seem to do for the soil what the earthworms do; that is, increase soil porosity or mix the topsoil.

Instead, the "white ants" (they really are beetles) tended to horde inside weather-proof colonies everything that they gather up. Until the colony died—and that may take as much as 100 years—and then finally erosion carried all the stores away and spread it out on the ground to be recycled.

But there was one curious and productive role that the termites may play. This stemmed from their mating habits; when the winged males sought a queen. All but one of them fails.

Small quantities of nitrogen, however, leave the mound in the bodies of the winged reproductives when they fly away from the nests. The vast majority of these perish without breeding . . . possibly their bodies make a significant contribution to nitrogen accession in areas of low rainfall, where little leaching of soluble salts occurs.
—*Rural Research,* No. 73, September, 1971

So the moral was clear: search hard enough and one will find a little good in everyone. Even a dead white ant.

The first point is that it (CSIRO) is a research institution, which is to be capable of doing research in the natural sciences . . . Secondly, this research must influence the progress of industry and agriculture in Australia. This statement requires further analysis, but what it means essentially is that new knowledge and understanding that results from our work must enable men on the land, the management of industry, government policy planners, economists, and indeed all of those who are concerned with the progress of this country, to have a new understanding of their affairs and to do things they have never done before.
—WHITE, SIR FREDERICK, "Administrative Problems in the Development of Scientific Research," *Public Administration,* 1968

The operative phrase here was "and to do things men have never done before."

Sir Frederick had it all there. A kindly, very patient and articulate gentleman, he had in his mind the pulse of the future, though his hands may have been bound in bureaucratic red tape and the mumblings of Parliaments long since wafted away by the winds of time.

". . . and to do things men had never done before."

And there was the destiny, if it was bold enough to embrace it, for "Australia 2000!"

Bibliography:

A

The American Scholar, publ for general circulation, by Phi Beta Kappa. Vol. 40, Summer 1971, No. 3

Australia. An Economic and Investment Reference, produced by The Australian News and Information Bureau, Wilke and Co. Ltd., Melbourne.

Australia (Official Handbook). The Specialty Press, Ltd., Victoria, 1967.

Australia. An Economic and Investment Reference, prod. by The Australian News and Information Bureau, Wilke and Co. Ltd., Melbourne, 1970.

Australia Handbook, Australia News and Information Bureau, Australian Govt. Publishing Service, 1972.

The Australian Environment, Commonwealth Scientific and Industrial Research Organization Halstead Press, Kingsgrove, N.S.W., 1949.

Australians in the Antarctic, Australian Govt. Publ. Service, Canberra, 1971.

B

Baker, Sidney J., *The Pacific Book of Australiana,* Angus & Robertson, 1967, Sydney.

Beatty, Bill, *Unique to Australia,* Ure Smith, Pty., Ltd., N. Sydney, 1968.

Bergamini, David and The Editors of Life, *The Land and Wildlife of Australia,* Time, Inc., N.Y., 1964.

Berndt, Ronald M., *Australian Aboriginal Art,* Ure Smith Pty., Ltd., The Macmillan Co., N.Y., 1964.

Bolton, A. T., *Walkabout's Australia,* Ure Smith Pty., Ltd., N. Sydney, 1968.

Bonython, Kym, *Modern Australian Painting 1960 to 1970,* Rigby Ltd., Adelaide, 1970.

Boyd, Robin, *The Australian Ugliness,* F. W. Cheshire, 1960, Victoria.

C

Cameron, Roderick, *Australia, History and Horizons,* Weidenfeld and Nicolson, London, 1971.

Clark, Manning, *A Short History of Australia,* Wm. Heinemann, Ltd., London, 1963.

Coghill, Ian, *Australia's Mineral Wealth,* Sorrett Publishing, Pty., Ltd., Melbourne, 1971. *CSIRO Research Index 1966.*

D

Davidson, B. R., *Australia: Wet or Dry?* Halstead Press, Pty., Ltd., Kingsgrove, N.S.W., 1969.

Davies, A. F. and Encel, S., *Australian Society,* F. W. Cheshire, Melbourne, 1970.

Dutton, Geoffrey and Harris, Max, *Australia's Censorship Crisis,* Sun Books, Melbourne, 1970.

F

Farwell, George, *Australian Landscapes,* Ure Smith, Pty., Ltd., N. Sydney, 1967.

Farwell, George, *Ghost Towns of Australia,* Rigby, Ltd., Adelaide, 1965.

G

Gelber, H. G., *The Australian American Alliance,* Penguin Books, Ltd., England, 1968.

Gilmore, Mary, *Selected Verse,* Angus & Robertson, Ltd., Sydney, 1948.

Goodman, Robert B. and Johnston, George, *The Australians,* Rigby Ltd., Adelaide, 1966.

Gunther, John, *Inside Australia,* Harper & Row, N.Y., 1972.

H

Hancock, W. K., *Australia,* Jacaranda Press, Pty., Ltd., Brisbane, 1966.

Harney, Bill, *Tales from the Aborigines,* Rigby, Ltd., Adelaide, 1959.

Hardy, Frank, *The Unlucky Australians,* Thomas Nelson, Ltd., Sydney, 1968.

Hill, Ernestine, *The Territory,* Angus and Robertson, Pty., Ltd., Sydney, 1951.

Hill, Ernestine, *Water into Gold,* Ure Smith, Pty., Ltd., N. Sydney, 1937.

Horne, Donald, *The Lucky Country,* Penguin Books, Ltd., England, 1964.

Horne, Donald, *The Next Australia,* Angus and Robertson, Pty., Ltd., Sydney, 1970.

I

Idriess, Ion L., *Challenge of the North,* Angus & Robertson, Pty, Ltd., Sydney, 1969.

Idriess, Ion L., *Lightning Ridge,* Angus & Robertson, Pty., Ltd., Sydney, 1944.

Idriess, Ion L., *The Wild North,* Angus & Robertson, Pty., Ltd., Sydney, 1960.

L

Lauder, Afferbeck, *Let Stalk Strine,* Ure Smith, Pty., Ltd., N. Sydney, 1965.

Law, Phillip, C.B.E., M.Sc., D.App.Sc., F.A.I.P., Adult Education Board of Tasmania, 1964.

Lawler, Ray, *Summer of the Seventeenth Doll,* Angus & Robertson, Great Britain, 1957.

Lawson, Henry, *Joe Wilson's Mates,* Lloyd O'Neil, Pty., Ltd., Victoria, 1970.

M

McGregor, Craig, *Profile of Australia,* Penguin Books, England, 1966.

Martin, Dr. Angus, *Pollution and Conservation in Australia,* Landsdowne Press, Pty., Ltd., Melbourne, 1971.

Marshall, Jock and Drysdale, Russell, *Journey Among Men,* Sun Books, Melbourne, 1966.

Masterman, G. G. (edited by), *Poverty in Australia,* Angus & Robertson, Pty., Ltd., Sydney, 1969.

Mikes, George, *Boomerang—Australia Rediscovered,* Andre Deutsch, Ltd., London, 1968.

Mills, Devon, editor, *Australian Management and Society,* Penguin Books, Australia, Ltd., 1971.

Moore, T. Inglis, *Social Patterns in Australian Literature,* Angus & Robertson, Pty., Ltd., Sydney, 1971.

O

Oakley, Barry, *Let's Hear it for Prendergast,* Penguin Books, England, 1971.

P

Paterson, A. B., *The Man From Snowy River,* Angus & Robertson, Pty., Ltd., Sydney, 1961.

Philipp, Franz, *Arthur Boyd,* Thames and Hudson, London, 1967.

Pringle, John Douglas, *On Second Thoughts,* Angus and Robertson, Ltd., Sydney, 1971.

Q

Queensland Alumina, edited by C. W. Allen, produced by General Public Relations, printed in Australia by Macarthur Press, no date.

R

Read, Kenneth E., *The High Valley,* Charles Scribner's Sons, N.Y., 1965.

Rienits, Rex and Thea, *A Pictorial History of Australia,* Paul Hamlyn, London, N.Y., Sydney, 1969.

Roberts, Ainslie and Mountford, Charles P., *The Dawn of Time,* Rigby, Ltd., Adelaide, 1969.

Roberts, Ainslie and Mountford, Charles P., *The Dreamtime,* Rigby, Ltd., Adelaide, 1965.

Roberts, Ainslie and Mountford, Charles P., *The First Sunrise,* Rigby, Ltd., Adelaide, 1971.

S

Serventy, Vincent, *Wildlife of Australia,* Thomas Nelson, Ltd., Australia, 1968.

Shute, Nevil, *The Far Country,* Wm. Heinemann, Ltd., London, 1952.

Shute, Nevil, *On The Beach,* Wm. Heinemann, Ltd., London, 1957.

Singleton, C. C. and Burke, David, *Railways of Australia,* Angus & Robertson, Pty., Ltd., Sydney, 1963.

Smith, Robin, *Australia in Colour,* Lansdowne Press, Pty., Ltd., Melbourne, 1963.

Stewart, Douglas and Keesing, Nancy, *The Pacific Book of Bush Ballads,* Angus & Robertson, Pty., Ltd., Sydney, 1967.

T

Tennant, Kylie, *The Battlers,* Angus & Robertson, Pty., Ltd., Sydney, 1941.

Turner, Ian, *The Australian Dream,* Sun Books, Pty., Ltd., Melbourne, 1968.

W

Wallace, Phyl and Noel, *Children of the Desert,* Thomas Nelson (Australia), Ltd., Melbourne, 1968.

Wannan, Bill, *The Black Stump and Beyond.* Ure Smith Pty., Ltd., Sydney, 1966.

Wannan, Bill, *My Kind of Country,* Rigby, Ltd., Adelaide, 1967.

Ward, Russel, *The Australian Legend,* Oxford University Press, London, 1958.

White, Patrick, *Voss,* The Viking Press, N.Y., 1957.

Wood, G. L., *Australia: Its Resources and Development,* The Macmillan Co., N.Y., 1947.

The Western Horizon of Victoria, Australia, Australian Publicity Council, Melbourne, no date.

White, Osmar, *Under The Iron Rainbow,* Wm. Heinemann, Ltd., Melbourne, London, 1969.

Y

Younger, R. M. *Australia and the Australians,* Humanities Press, New York, 1970.

Periodicals:

If one wants to know something about a country, whether it is his own or one that is strange to him, a good way is to read the daily (or weekly) newspapers.

Not just the headlines, but the editorials, the comics, the sports and financial sections, even fashions and society, and — most of all — the classified section.

It is in the classified section that one learns what skills the society feels it needs (or wants) — and those it doesn't (jobs wanted), how much housing is available and at what price.

The classified is more than a caricature; it can be read as a Gothic novel of infinite chapters, layer by layer, as in peeling an onion. One who learns to mine this rich strata finds out much more about the society, and himself, than he ever could from the front page news or the editorials.

As background for this book, seven newspapers were read assiduously day by day for nearly six months, and sporadically over a period of more than three years.

For the purpose of this book, the ones most useful were, *The Australian, The Age,* the *Sydney Morning Herald,* the *Canberra Times,* and the *Australian Financial Review.* Clippings and quotes from these are presented throughout the book.

The Australian press appears to differ from its counterpart in the United States in that it seems to be more free, more down to earth, breezier and happier. In some ways it is closer to what has been called in the U. S., "the underground press." It seems to have writers instead of mere reporters . . . and therein lies the difference.

There is a rich pungency to it, as if stirred — even in Melbourne and Sydney — by a strong wind from the "outback."

Index: